SKY WARRIORS

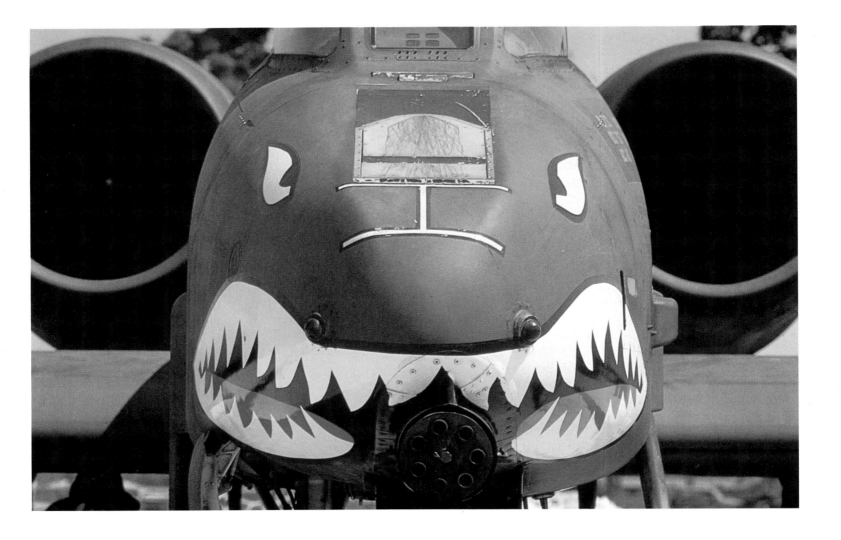

SKY WARRIORS

Combat Aircraft of the '90s

Christopher Chant

Brian Trodd Publishing House Limited

Published in 1991 by
Brian Trodd Publishing House Limited
27 Swinton Street, London WC1X 9NW

ISBN 1 85361 203 0

Printed in Italy

PHOTO ACKNOWLEDGMENTS

All photographs supplied by the Department of Defense,
Still Media Records Center, with the exception of the
following: Nikk Burridge, 5; Fairchild, 31; General
Dynamics, 27 top left; McDonnell Douglas, 9; 13 bottom,
20 bottom, 21, 36 top, 38 top, 48 top and bottom;
Northrop, 58 top, 59; TRH Pictures/DoD, title page, 57;
Westinghouse, 25 bottom.

CONTENTS

AIR SUPERIORITY
The Control of Airspace

Lift-off for an F-14A of VF-33 'Tarsiers'

The air arms of the United States are the Western world's most important and capable air forces. They have reached this pre-eminent position through a combination of large numbers of warplanes, dedicated and highly skilled personnel, and a constant striving to secure the technological edge over their potential opponents. The overall mission of the US Air Force (and by extension its sister air arms) has been concisely summarized as: 'to organize, train and equip aerospace forces to deter aggression and, if necessary, defeat aggressors across the spectrum of conflict'.

The air arms in question are the United States Air Force, US Naval Aviation, the air arm of the US Marine Corps, and US Army Aviation.

Above: An F-14A is positioned on one of the Constellation's *catapults during Naval Air Reserve carrier qualifications.*
Right: These F-15 Eagles are aircraft of the Alaskan Air Command's 21st Tactical Fighter Wing.
Below: F-15s of the 18th TFW's 67th Tactical Fighter Squadron on the flight line at Nyutabaru Air Base.

At the heart of the American air capabilities is air superiority, for this superiority allows all other parts of the American air machine to operate under optimum operational conditions. Air superiority is defined as the winning and subsequent retention of the degree of airspace dominance sufficient to prevent prohibitive enemy interference with one's own operations.

Air superiority fighters are designed to clear airspace of enemy aircraft and are generally fairly large machines possessing very high outright performance in terms of speed, climb rate and range. Such fighters are also fitted with advanced sensors (radar, infra-red or visual) that can detect and acquire potential targets at long range, and then track them as they are sorted into order of threat. The targets are then tackled in the appropriate threat order by weapons optimized for long, medium, short and dogfighting ranges.

The two most important fighters of this type currently in service with the American forces are the USAF's McDonnell Douglas F-15 Eagle and US Naval Aviation's Grumman F-14 Tomcat.

The USAF has a requirement for more than 1,000 Eagles of three basic types: 420 or more of the initial F-15A single-seat and F-15B two-seat combat-capable trainer models, 460 or more of the upgraded and updated F-15C single-seat and F-15D two-seat models, and 200 of the F-15E two-seat strike model. These aircraft serve with Tactical Air Command, Pacific Air Forces, US Air Forces in Europe, and Alaskan Air Command.

Typical operators of the Eagle in its primary air superiority role are the 22nd, 53rd and 525th Tactical Fighter Squadrons of the 36th Tactical Fighter Wing, located at Bitburg Air Base in Germany. The 36th TFW is a component of the USAFE's 17th Air Force, part of the North Atlantic Treaty Organizations's 4th Allied Tactical Air Force. Together with other 4th ATAF assets, the 36th TFW is tasked with providing

air superiority over southern Germany. This was considered one of the most important and difficult tasks faced by the NATO allies up to the end of the 'Cold War', and although the threat of an offensive by Warsaw Pact forces is now considered much smaller, a high level of readiness is maintained.

Bitburg is located in the Eifel mountains of what was West Germany before the reunification of East and West Germany in 1990. Here, quick reaction to possible threats is important, and the base keeps four F-15C Eagles on 'Zulu Alert' for minimum-delay despatch.

The four aircraft are kept in a special alert facility at one end of the runway. Unlike the shelters accommodating the rest of the base's combat aircraft, this facility is not hardened against attack by the enemy's counter-air fighters, for the simple reason that the aircraft should be in the air at any time that an enemy might launch an attack. The facility accommodates two pairs of aircraft flanking a central administration and recreation block. The aircraft of the primary and secondary leaders are in the inner bays immediately adjacent to the central block, on the right and left respectively, with the aircraft of their wingmen in the two outer bays.

The central block has three floors. On the ground floor, from front to back, are the security section, the administration and kitchen sections, the main lateral passage (with stairs to the first floor and 'fireman' poles so that the crew can slide rapidly down to the ground floor), and the toilet and store sections. On the first floor, from front to back, are the 'battle cab', the briefing room, the lounge with easy chairs and a TV, the main lateral passage, a cinema and toilet, and the stairs. On the second floor, from front to back, are four separate pilot bunks, six crew chief and facility staff bunks, the main lateral passage, a store and bathroom, and the stairs.

The aircraft bays have fronts that are completely open so that the fighters can move out quickly, and rears with doors wide and tall enough to allow the engine exhausts to stream straight out of the bay.

The central block provides self-contained facilities for the men on Zulu Alert, who operate 24-hour shifts. The recreational aspects of the facility help to keep the pilots rested but alert, though many Zulu Alert pilots find their duty periods ideal for catching up with paperwork. The pilots make frequent visits to the 'battle cab', which overlooks the airfield and contains essential details of weather, flight routes and other tactical information. One of the main tasks of the facility's staff is keeping this vital information completely up to date.

Unlike the pilots, crew chiefs are generally allocated to the Zulu Alert facility on a full-time basis, serving one 24-hour duty period every three days. The crew chiefs are by common consent the best on the base, and their task is to ensure that each of the four F-15Cs is ready to scramble at less than a moment's notice. This is an exacting task at the purely technical level, and the crew chiefs have also to bear in mind that the aircraft in their charge are permanently loaded with live ordnance for full operational capability day and night, 365 days per year.

Other key members of the alert facility are the teams in charge of maintenance and security. The men of the maintenance crew tend to the needs of the pilots and crew chiefs, and also ensure that the facility is kept scrupulously clean and tidy so that no one is tripped or otherwise delayed during a scramble. In addition to their ordinary security tasks, the men of the security crew fulfil a similar function in ensuring as rapid a scramble as possible by preventing any outside interference.

All Bitburg's Zulu Alert scrambles originate with surveillance radar operators in southern Germany. Whether operating ground-based radars or the powerful airborne system of the Boeing E-3 Sentry AWACS, these men and women track all air traffic in their sector, immediately reporting any suspicious track to Sector Operations Center III, a concrete-buried facility proof against nuclear attack. SOC III is responsible for all air movement in the 4th ATAF region, and if the SOC III commander agrees that a track is suspicious, he informs Bitburg, where the base operations staff sound the klaxon in the Zulu Alert facility.

The sounding of the klaxon is the signal for apparently frantic but in fact carefully organized and well rehearsed activity inside the alert facility. The crew chiefs rush to their aircraft and pilots slide down the poles to reach the ground floor of the administrative centre before dashing through the side doors into the bays, where the crew chiefs are completing their pre-flight preparations.

Right: A KC-135A Stratotanker prepares to refuel an F-15 Eagle of the 18th TFW during a redeployment exercise from Kadena AB in Okinawa to Tyndall AFB in Florida.

Within a very few moments of the klaxon's blare, each pilot is scrambling up the access ladder into his cockpit, where he straps into the ejector seat and dons the helmet waiting on the cockpit rail. The pilots' next actions are determined by two lights: a green light indicates an immediate scramble, while a red light indicates that SOC III has called the aircraft to battle stations. In the latter case the pilots sit in their cockpits and wait for the next order, which may be a stand-down if the suspicious track turns away, or a scramble if the suspicious aircraft continues on course.

In the event of a scramble, the starboard engine is started first to provide electrical power for the fighter's systems, including the all-important inertial navigation system. This has to be reset each time the fighter starts, so the pilot's next

task is to enter Bitburg's co-ordinates into the INS. As this process continues, the crew chief completes his check of the fighter and removes any covers still in place. When he has completed this task, the crew chief removes the access ladder, and the pilot fires up the port engine.

It takes three minutes for the INS to come on line, and in this time the pilot receives radio information about the tactical situation, including initial heading, interception co-ordinates, the precise nature of the sortie, and the degree of urgency attached to the mission. When this has been completed, the F-15C is ready to move.

Other events that have been completed in this interval are the protection of the alert facility by an armed security detachment, and the clearance of the runway for the Zulu

Alert fighters by diverting aircraft on the ground onto taxiways and putting aircraft already in the air into a holding pattern. Right through this period, SOC III can cancel the alert if the suspicious track turns away or otherwise loses significance. Many of the alerts are in fact 'Tango' training missions, though the pilots do not know this until they are airborne, and many 'Alpha' operational missions become 'Tango' missions if the track that caused the alert ceases to be suspicious.

During a 'Tango' mission, the fighters carry out interceptions on each other, or on other NATO fighters in the area. A Zulu Alert is called about nine times each week on average.

The pilots seldom try to guess whether each alert is an 'Alpha' or 'Tango' mission, and therefore treat each mission as though it is the real thing. As soon as the take-off order is received, two F-15Cs nose out of their hangar bays and move onto the runway. The alert facility is located as close to the runway as possible, and the short high-speed taxiway connecting the two is kept immaculately clean to prevent the possibility of engine damage through foreign object ingestion.

The two fighters turn onto the runway without halting, ignite their afterburners and accelerate to take-off speed. As soon as his fighter has rotated and lifted off, each pilot retracts the landing gear of his machine and pulls into a steep climbing turn.

Left: A pair of F-15 Eagle air-superiority fighters lifts off from Bitburg AB in Germany in the slightly echeloned formation of leader and wingman.

Above: Cockpit-eye view of a 67th TFW F-15 Eagle lining up for take-off from Korat Royal Air Force Base in Thailand during the 'Commando West IX' US/Thai training exercise.

Since the klaxon first sounded, only four minutes have passed. USAF doctrine allows five minutes to this point, but is is a matter of professional pride by the Zulu Alert crews to beat this figure by as handsome a margin as possible. Only now, with the primary pair en route to the planned interception point, do the pilots of the secondary pair shut down their engines and return to the recreation area.

Below: Two F-15 Eagle fighters of the 57th Fighter Interceptor Squadron, based at Keflavik Naval Air Station in Iceland, formate on a Soviet Tupolev Tu-95 'Bear'.

Above: The USAF is geared for operation capability 24 hours per day, as evidenced by this F-15 Eagle fighter on the ramp at Misawa AB during a visit to Japan.

The fighters of the primary pair climb rapidly and steer onto the intercept course. Speed in this phase of the mission is governed by the urgency of the overall situation. If the potential target is making slowly or irregularly toward the German border, transit speed is kept low; but if the potential target is heading from the east at high speed, transit speed is as high as possible. Pilots generally try to maintain visual flight conditions, but as their task is day or night interceptions under any and all weather conditions, this is often impossible.

The interception itself falls into any one of several categories, the highest threat rating being given to any track that may signal the beginning of a pre-emptive air strike by the Warsaw Pact. Clearly such an eventuality played a major part in 4th ATAF's thinking up to 1989, and is still an important factor in NATO considerations. But it has always been of great importance to differentiate between armed aircraft that may herald the beginning of a major Warsaw Pact offensive, and a formation of aircraft that may have strayed toward or even over the border because of navigation error. Thus analysis of the potential target's intention is a high priority both for SOC III and for the ground-controlled intercept radar unit vectoring the primary pair toward their interception.

A hostile intrusion into German airspace would clearly have to be met with force. However, the inadvertent straying of a Warsaw Pact warplane over the border would need more careful handling if an international incident was to be avoided. In the recent past, the mere presence of the American fighters was generally sufficient to cause the intruder to withdraw over the border, though the possibility of a few warning shots was kept in reserve.

In fact most Zulu Alert sorties are flown to help Western aircraft that have strayed close to Germany's eastern border and its prohibited Air Defence Identification Zone. The Warsaw Pact air-defence organization had a well-deserved reputation for firing first and asking questions afterward, so the shepherding of innocent aircraft away from danger was and is a major task of Zulu Alert fighters on 'Alpha' missions. Most interceptions of such strayed aircraft are achieved well short of the ADIZ, but when the stray has already crossed into the ADIZ, even the Zulu Alert fighters have to secure special authorization to enter the zone. Zulu Alert fighters also intercepted and escorted the aircraft of occasional defectors in or near the ADIZ. In both cases, the American pilots used the 'sign language' of the International Civil Aviation Organization to communicate, with wing rocking used to indicate 'follow me', lowered landing gear to indicate 'follow me and land' etc.

In these circumstances the identification of the aircraft and their intentions remains basically simple. More problematical is the analysis of the intentions of military aircraft operating near the ADIZ. Here the standard procedure is the identification of the plane, then an attempt to grasp its intentions. If he can determine these, the Eagle pilot discusses with SOC III the action to be taken in the given situation.

In general, the fighters seek to approach the target from behind as this offers the most advantageous position should an attack be necessary. In this approach, the fighters are vectored by the GCI controller, and also use their own APG-63

Above: Air-to-air view of an F-15C Eagle of the 32nd TFS, from Soesterberg AB in the Netherlands, during a 'Zulu Alert' with AIM-7 Sparrow and AIM-9 Sidewinder missiles

Below: An F-15 in full afterburner lifts off the runway at Florida's Eglin AFB during Exercise 'Nomad Thrust '88'.

or APG-70 radar in semi-autonomous mode to find any target or targets, flying higher or lower than the Eagle, out to a maximum range of 185 miles. When it entered service in 1974, the Eagle was notable not only for this powerful radar but also for its HOTAS (Hands-On-Throttle-And-Stick) cockpit, the first in a production fighter of the type in which the pilot can leave his left hand on the throttles and his right hand on the control column, which in addition to operating the fighter's control surfaces also accommodates all major controls for the radar, head-up display and weapons.

The primary weapons of the F-15 are the AIM-7 Sparrow medium-range and AIM-9 Sidewinder short-range air-to-air missiles, together with an M61A1 Vulcan 20mm cannon for heavy firepower in the dogfighting regime. The standard missile armament is four Sparrows carried on ejector launchers on the undersides of the engine trunks, and four Sidewinders carried on the inner pair of the four underwing hardpoints. The AIM-7M version of the Sparrow weighs 503lb (228kg), and uses semi-active radar homing to reach targets out to a maximum range of 62 miles (100km) after a high-altitude launch; its 86lb (39kg) warhead is exploded by impact or proximity fuses. The AIM-9L version of the shorter-ranged but more agile Sidewinder weighs 188lb (85kg), and uses passive infra-red homing to reach targets out to a maximum range of 11 miles (18km); its 22.5lb (10.2kg) warhead is exploded by an active laser proximity fuse.

The main limitation of the Sparrow is its guidance. This requires the attacking fighter to continue on course toward

the target until missile detonation, for only thus can the target be 'illuminated' by the fighter's radar and so provide the reflected electromagnetic energy needed by the missile's semi-active radar guidance. This limitation should be removed early in the 1990s by the advent of the AIM-130 AMRAAM. This Advanced Medium-Range Air-to-Air Missile was designed to offer the performance of the Sparrow with little more than the Sidewinder's weight and size, together with advanced guidance. There have been considerable development problems with the type, which weighs 335lb (152kg) and possesses a maximum range of 45 miles (72km) from a high altitude launch; the 45lb (20kg) warhead is detonated by impact or proximity fuses. Most advanced of the missile's features, however, is the guidance package. This comprises an inertial platform, pre-programmed before launch but updatable in flight by the launch fighter's radar, for the midcourse phase of the flight, and active radar for the terminal phase of the flight. The result is a missile that can be left to its own devices soon after launch, allowing the launch fighter to turn away toward safer areas.

In the F-15 scenario, once any potential target has been investigated and declared harmless, or otherwise shepherded away from the ADIZ, the primary pair can return to Bitburg. After the fighters have landed, returned to their alert facility bays, and been entrusted once more to their crew chiefs, the pilots undergo first an intelligence debriefing and second a general debriefing. The second is concerned with the mission, the tactics, and the performance of the two pilots, and is concerned with improving pilots' tactical skills.

US Naval Aviation's counterpart to the Eagle is the classic Grumman F-14 tomcat. More than 500 of these powerful variable-geometry warplanes are operational in the original F-14A version. There are also a few of the F-14A Plus version with more effective engines, and more than 400 F-14As are to be rebuilt to F-14D(R) improved standard with digital electronics in place of the F-14A's analog electronics. The Tomcat is operated by 25 squadrons, and the type is operated by most of the 13 active and two reserve carrier air groups that provide air capability for the US Navy's force of 14 aircraft-carriers, each the core of a multi-capable carrier battle group.

Long-range defence of the carrier battle group is the main task undertaken by the Tomcat, whose typical target is the supersonic bomber able to launch two nuclear-armed missiles at a range of 185 miles (298km) from their target. Such an attack on an American carrier battle group would probably be made by a squadron of 18 to 20 aircraft (able to salvo 36 to 40 missiles) with its flights approaching from different directions at different heights, and possibly at night and in distinctly marginal weather conditions, to make the defence's task that much more difficult. Even so, it is telling evidence of the Tomcat's capabilities that the US Navy remains firmly committed to this type despite a first flight as far back as December 1970.

The Tomcat was designed as a weapons system, carrying a two-man crew (front-seat pilot and rear-seat radar intercept officer) to make optimum use of the long-range AWG-9 radar and associated fire-control system in conjunction with a comprehensive array of air-to-air weapons. These range from the AIM-54 Phoenix (the world's longest-ranged air-to-air missile), to the medium-range AIM-7 Sparrow, and finally to the short-range AIM-9 Sidewinder. The Tomcat also accommodates an M61A1 Vulcan 20mm cannon, a six-barrel weapon of the rotary-barrel type offering a very high rate of fire (typically 4,000 rounds per minute) in the dogfighting role.

While the Tomcat's advanced sensors, computing equipment and weapons make possible fully independent operations, the type was also designed to make full use of the advantages offered by collaborative operations. Thus the Tomcat has an automatic data-link system that allows information to be provided on a real-time basis from ships' long-range surveillance radars, or by the sensors carried on aircraft such as the Grumman E-2C Hawkeye airborne early warning and Grumman EA-6B Prowler electronic warfare platforms. Linkage with these long-range sensors is designed to provide Tomcat crews with sufficiently early warning to

Below: Superb air-to-air view of a lightly armed F-14A Tomcat of VF-84 'Jolly Rogers', a component of the carrier air wing of the nuclear-powered carrier Nimitz.

Above: An F-14A of VF-142 'Ghostriders' from the Dwight D. Eisenhower *escorts a Tu-95 'Bear-D' reconnaissance type.*

allow them to intercept attackers well beyond missile launch range. This is clearly the most desirable solution, for it limits target numbers to the enemy's aircraft, which are large and therefore comparatively straightforward to detect and destroy. If the enemy force does manage to launch missiles, these immediately become the primary targets, and though they cannot take evasive action, these present greater interception problems because of their larger numbers and small size.

The Tomcat's fleet defence role has two major subdivisions, in the form of the combat air patrol and the deck-launch intercept. The CAP is usually operated by a pair of Tomcats. These operate at a radius of about 175 miles (282km) from their parent carrier, and are supported by a Hawkeye positioned about 55 miles (88km) farther out from the carrier. With a load of four Phoenixes, two Sparrows, two Sidewinders and 675 rounds of 20mm ammunition as well as two drop tanks, the Tomcat can patrol for about two hours at this radius, generally at an altitude of approximately 25,000 feet (7,620m). The DLI, on the other hand, comprises a pair of fully armed and fueled Tomcats sitting on their catapults ready for immediate launch.

The mission begins with the all-important briefing, which takes about one hour and covers factors as diverse as weather conditions, emergency procedures, operating station, call signs, the mission's operational rationale, and possible occurrences together with the appropriate pre-planned reactions. With the briefing concluded, crews move to their aircraft and run carefully through their pre-flight checks to ensure that there are no obvious defects (leaks etc), that all the control surfaces are moving freely, and that all pressures and temperatures are within nominal limits. The Tomcat is fitted with comprehensive BITE (Built-In Test Equipment), and this is an invaluable aid to the early diagnosis of electronic faults. The AWG-9 system is very complex and, being of the analog type, more susceptible to fault than modern digital electronics. If one of the radar modes is not working properly, the BITE's computer can decide if the system is still capable of fulfilling its task or if the problem can be evaded by use of another mode as back-up.

Below left: An F-14A of VF-32 'Swordsmen' lights its afterburners before launching from the Mediterranean-based 6th Fleet's carrier John F. Kennedy.
Below: Flight crew briefing in the VF-143 'Pukin' Dogs' ready room aboard the Dwight D. Eisenhower

The tasks of the two crew members are carefully defined. The pilot is the commander, undertakes air-to-air communications, has sole responsibility for the short-range armament (Vulcan and Sidewinder) and has a say in the selection and management of the longer-range weapons (Sparrow and Phoenix). The RIO has sole responsibility for the radar and weapon-control system, and therefore has in front of him the display concerned with the overall tactical situation as revealed by the radar and data-link communication. This makes the RIO better suited than the pilot to decide on initial tactics for interception and engagement though, as commander, the pilot can override his RIO's suggestions. Targets and missile launch are both recommended by the weapon system computer, but the RIO can override both on the basis of his own appreciation of the evolving tactical situation. The RIO is also responsible for navigation and management of the electronic countermeasures system.

The pilot and RIO are paired as long as possible, and this close association is important in creating the spirit of teamwork that gives each officer a keen insight into his partner's capabilities. This is very important in the whole range of tactical situations, and becomes vitally important if the range closes to the dogfight stage, in which the RIO acts as another pair of eyes for the pilot. Here he uses his own skills and the excellent rearward field of vision provided by the roomy canopy to keep the pilot, who should keep his concentration fixed on the situation to his front, fully advised about conditions to the Tomcat's sides and rear. It is worth noting, though, that the pilot does have three rear-view mirrors.

After completing their check of the Tomcat, the crew board the fighter via the extending ladder in the port side of the fuselage. Once installed in their ejector seats, the pilot and RIO strap in, complete all their electrical and pneumatic connections, and stow the safety pins whose removal arms their ejector seats. The engines are started, the ladder is retracted, and the long canopy hinges down from the rear to lock into its closed position.

The pilot now taxies toward his allocated catapult. As he reaches this position, a baffle is raised from the deck by hydraulic power to deflect the jet exhaust upward: without the baffle, the danger area behind the exhaust nozzles would stretch back some 500ft (150m) almost to the rear end of the flight deck.

When his fighter is in position, the pilot shortens the nosewheel leg by about 14in (36cm) to 'kneel' the Tomcat, and lowers the launch bar that fits into the catapult shuttle. Finally checks are completed both inside and outside the fighter. The pilot runs up his two engines first to full military power and then through the five stages of afterburning. After the pilot and catapult officer have exchanged ready signals, the catapult is fired. This accelerates the weighty fighter to 173mph (278km/h) in just 2.5 seconds. As the Tomcat leaves the catapult, the nosewheel leg extends automatically, increasing the wings' angle of attack, and the machine surges into the air almost without pilot input. As soon as the Tomcat has cleared the edge of the flight deck, the pilot pulls his machine into a sharp climbing turn to port and retracts the landing gear. Only moments later, the throttles are pulled back to normal cruising power, and the climb to transit altitude continues at about 340mph (547km/h). With transit altitude reached, the Tomcat cruises to its patrol area at about Mach 0.7, a speed calculated for economy of time and fuel.

Above: An F-14A Tomcat of VF-24 'Renegades' of the Kitty Hawk's *carrier air wing launches as crash crews stand by in damage-control vehicles.*

It is worth noting that during a DLI, full afterburner is retained for the climb to operational altitude, during which the right intercept heading is adopted, and transit is made at Mach 1.5 to that the attackers can be intercepted as far from the carrier as possible. This severely reduces the Tomcat's radius of action because of the very high fuel consumption rate in afterburning mode. It is therefore standard practice during a DLI to launch a Grumman KA-6D intruder tanker immediately after the pair of fighters to provide inflight-refuelling capability for the Tomcats' return to the carrier.

During a CAP patrol, the two Tomcats (leader and wingman) cruise as economically as possible. If warning of possible intruders or attackers is data-linked from a Hawkeye, the fighters immediately go to full afterburner and accelerate to maximum speed, in the process sweeping their wings back to 68°, and start to scan with their own radars. Despite the inevitable fuel consumption rate penalty, maximum acceleration and speed are desirable for two compelling reasons: it puts the interception point as far distant from the carrier as possible, and also gives the missile(s) maximum kinetic energy at launch. This latter gives the missile(s) extra speed and more range, in the process providing considerably greater manoeuvre capability at the end of the flight, reducing missile flight time, and improving kill probability to a significant degree.

From the beginning of the programme, Grumman designed the Tomcat as an uncompromised air superiority fighter with the volume, size, and weight-carrying capability to absorb the 1,293lb (586.5kg) AWG-9 system and its associated Phoenix missile without compromising performance. Thus the wing-sweep mechanism is completely automatic, and provides the best sweep angle for any particular sector of the flight regime, though the pilot has the ability to override the automatic system in circumstances such as low-speed acceleration.

As a result, the Tomcat has exceptional control characteristics from Mach 2 right down to 115mph (185km/h). Though the Tomcat was designed primarily as a high-speed missile platform, it is still well able to hold its own in dogfights, where speed bleeds off rapidly in the sustained

Above: With its wings spread, high-lift devices deployed, and landing gear and arrester hook lowered, an F-14A prepares to land on the Kitty Hawk *after a sortie.*

turning of such encounters. At very low speeds, with the wings fully extended at 20° sweep, the Tomcat's roll rate is comparatively low, but its rate of turn is exceptional for a machine of its size. At the same time there are few limitations on angle of attack up to 60°. This is not as high as the figure attainable by modern fighters such as the McDonnell Douglas F/A-18 Hornet, but better than the figure for contemporaries such as the F-15 Eagle.

The one area where the F-14A is deficient is in the powerplant. This was inherited from the F-111B naval version of the General Dynamics F-111 multi-role warplane, an abortive type that the Tomcat was designed to replace, and comprises a pair of 20,900lb (9,480kg) afterburning thrust Pratt & Whitney TF30-P-412 turbofans. This engine type was

not designed for the fighter role, which demands frequent throttle movements and flexible functioning under adverse airflow conditions, and means that the throttles of the F-14A must be handled with delicacy and preferably left in a forward (high-power) setting in high-g manoeuvres at high angles of attack if the engines are not to stall.

This is one of the main reasons why the F-14D(R) will be re-engined with two examples of the 23,100lb (10,480kg) afterburning thrust General Electric F110-GE-400 turbofan, which was designed as a fighter engine and is therefore far less susceptible to frequent and fast throttle movements under all flight conditions. The engines also offer more power and have a higher thrust/weight ratio, and will therefore give the Tomcat sprightlier rates of climb and acceleration.

Below: Carrier decks can get very crowded, as suggested by this shot of F-14As on the Kitty Hawk. *The apparent chaos is really a well-organized traffic system.*

The AWG-9 radar is a particularly potent system. Water-cooled and occupying a volume of 28 cu ft (0.79m³), this was the world's first radar with track-while-scan and effective look-down capabilities. The radar can acquire and track 24 targets out to a maximum range of 137 miles (220km). The computerized fire-control system can then decide which six of these pose the greatest threat, and simultaneously engage them with six Phoenix missiles, each of them code-keyed to a specific target. Under these circumstances, verification of a possible target as an enemy plane is very important, and this is greatly aided by the Northrop Television Camera Set carried under the nose: this can lock onto the target at long range and provide the crew with an image sufficiently clear and accurate for positive identification. The system also provides a useful back-up in the event of radar failure.

The AIM-54A version of the Phoenix missile weighs 985lb (447kg) and possesses a maximum range in excess of 125 miles (201km). After launch from the Tomcat, the missile climbs to a peak altitude of 81,200ft (24,750m) under control of its onboard autopilot with its onboard radar in semi-active mode to home onto that part of the launch fighter's radar energy reflected by the target. The missile then dives toward the target, converting its altitude into kinetic energy for greater manoeuvrability in the terminal phase of the attack. The final 12.4 miles (20km) of the attack are made with the missile's radar in active search mode for extreme accuracy. The 132lb (59.9kg) warhead is sufficiently large to destroy virtually any airborne target when initiated by actual impact with the target or alternatively by its infra-red or radar proximity fuses.

The other two American fighters capable of undertaking the air superiority role are the McDonnell Douglas F/A-18 Hornet and the General Dynamics F-16 Fighting Falcon, which are both dual-role types optimized for the fighter and attack roles.

The Hornet is a fairly radical derivative, developed collaboratively by McDonnell Douglas and Northrop, of the latter's YF-17 prototype that in January 1975 was declared loser to the YF-16 prototype of the Fighting Falcon in the USAF's 1973 Light-Weight Fighter competition.

The spur for the type's development was the approaching obsolescence of two of US Naval Aviation's mainstays, namely the McDonnell Douglas F-4 Phantom II multi-role fighter and the Vought A-7 Corsair II light/medium attack plane. Space is always at a premium on an aircraft carrier, and it was decided that the technology was ripe for the development of a single basic airframe that could undertake the fully optimized fighter and attack roles. The resulting VFAX specification was issued in 1974, and originally envisaged an F-18 fighter and A-18 attack plane that would accrue considerable production and carrier stowage economies by being variants of a single basic airframe.

It later became clear that careful design and modern software would allow the same airframe to be used for both tasks, with role optimization provided by the loading of different software into the Hornet's mission computer. Thus was born the F/A-18 that first flew in November 1979 and entered service in 1983 after a protracted but very fruitful development programme that considerably enhanced the Hornet's flight, mission and payload capabilities. The Hornet is now used by the air arms of the US Navy and US Marine Corps, the former having a requirement for some 800 aircraft and the latter for 350 aircraft.

In the air superiority role, the type is deployed as an alternative to the Tomcat especially in the slightly smaller

Above: An F/A-18A Hornet of the US Navy's 'Blue Angels' display team provides a nice silhouette of the Hornet dual-role carrierborne and land-based warplane.

aircraft carriers tasked with operations in lower-threat areas. The Hornet is operated in much the same basic way as the Tomcat, though there are of course detail differences largely because of the type's operation by just the pilot. This places great emphasis on the Hornet's electronic and display systems, which are among the most advanced in the world.

The core of the weapon system is the APG-65 radar, a water-cooled equipment capable of tracking 10 targets and displaying those eight possessing the most threatening tracks. In the Hornet's fighter role, the radar progresses from the range-while-search mode, which has 92 mile (150km) range, to track-while-scan mode, which is matched to the AIM-7 Sparrow missile and has 46 mile (74km) range, to its raid-assessment mode, which has 35 mile (56km) range, and finally to short-range fire-control modes, which have 23 mile (37km) and 6 mile (10km) ranges for use of the AIM-9 Sidewinder short-range air-to-air missile and M61A1 Vulcan cannon.

Data are displayed on the pilot's head-up display and three head-down displays, and in common with HOTAS controls this provides an operational flexibility of unparalleled versatility. The two central computers are high-speed digital

Right: An F/A-18 of VFA-86 'Sidewinders' climbs steeply to show off the thoroughbred lines of the Hornet dual-role fighter and attack warplane.
Below: An F/A-18 breaks away from its partner. Both Hornets carry two AIM-9 Sidewinders and large drop tanks.

Above: F-16Cs of the 17th TFS are serviced at Shaw AFB.

units that handle all basic flight and mission work, leaving the pilot free to concentrate on the evolving tactical situation and call up any additional information he may want.

The Hornet carries an air-to-air armament of two AIM-7 Sparrows and two AIM-9 Sidewinders, which is perhaps too light a load when the type may be faced with the task of dealing with a saturation attack on its parent carrier. To this extent, therefore, the Hornet is clearly inferior to the Tomcat, which also possesses a longer radius of action. On the other side of the tactical coin, the Hornet is a superior dogfighter to the Tomcat, especially at high angles of attack.

The F-16 Fighting Falcon is the USAF's counterpart to the F/A-18 in the operational sense, and also possesses a conceptual relationship as it resulted from the YF-16 prototype that won the Light-Weight Fighter competition over the YF-17 that led eventually to the F/A-18. In numerical terms, the Fighting Falcon is by far the most important American warplane, for the USAF currently deploys more than 725 of the initial F-16A single-seat and F-16B two-seat versions, with deliveries continuing of the improved F-16C single-seat and F-16D two-seat versions, of which 1,936 are required.

The F-16A and F-16B have APG-66 radar and the choice between two variants of the same turbofan, namely the 23,830 or 25,000lb (10,810 or 11,340kg) afterburning thrust Pratt & Whitney F100-P-100 or F100-P-200. The F-16C and F-16D

Below: An F-16B of the 430th TFS at Nellis AFB is marshalled out for a deployment flight to El Libertador AB, Venezuela.

feature a number of aerodynamic and structural improvements, carry the improved APG-68 radar, and have the choice between the two engine types, namely the 27,600 or 23,450lb (12,520 or 10,640kg) afterburning thrust General Electric F110-GE-100 or Pratt & Whitney F100-P-220.

The USAF had planned to deploy a total of 40 tactical fighter wings by the early 1990s, but recent budgetary restrictions have forced the service to trim this total back from the 36 of the late 1980s to just 35. Of these 35 regular air force wings, 27 are equipped with the Fighting Falcon, which also serves with four wings of the Air Force Reserve and nine wings of the Air National Guard.

The Fighting Falcon was born as a result of the lessons learned the hard way during the Vietnam War by the USAF. In this South-East Asian conflict, the USAF discovered that its Mach 2+ tactical aircraft were very capable in their designed operational tasks, but also so complex that they were difficult to maintain under adverse conditions. America also found to its cost that in many respect these tactical aircraft were too good for their task. North Vietnam had only a small air force flying what appeared to be technically obsolescent aircraft such as the Soviet-built Mikoyan-Gurevich MiG-17 'Fresco', MiG-19 'Farmer' and MiG-21 'Fishbed' fighters. When these light and therefore cheap and relatively easily maintained fighters got into close action with their larger and theoretically superior American counterparts, the USAF pilots found that unless they scored a missile victory at medium or short range, they became embroiled in a dogfight situation. Here a succession of manoeuvres would bleed off the American fighters' energy, reducing speed to well below Mach 1 and shifting the odds towards the North Vietnamese pilots in their considerably nimbler fighters armed with devastating short-range cannon.

The USAF rightly reasoned that it needed a new breed of tactical fighter offering performance that was still high, but not as high as that offered by machines such as the McDonnell Douglas F-4 Phantom II, in an airframe that was small and configured for a far greater level of manoeuvrability than the fighters of the time. The new fighter would also have to be considerably more maintainable in its airframe, engine and electronics.

To prove the technology for such a fighter, the USAF launched its Light-Weight Fighter competition, and General Dynamics responded with its Model 401 design that first flew as the YF-16 in February 1974, and was declared winner of the LWF competition in January 1975. The type had shown such exceptional capabilities that it was ordered into production, and the initial F-16A flew in December 1976.

This is still a remarkable design, and for its time was an epoch-making breakthrough in fighter evolution. The airframe is based on a beautiful fuselage whose sleek contours are blended into those of the wings for minimum drag, and the flying surfaces have only moderate sweep to provide great agility rather than very high performance.

From the start the type was planned round a 'fly-by-wire' control system in an inherently unstable (and therefore potentially more manoeuvrable) airframe. In this type of fighter, the computer is required to fly the machine at all times, the pilot's inputs via a sidestick controller then being interpreted by the computer and translated into electrical

Right: A crew chief waits to launch two F-16Cs of the 10th TFS during a 'Saber Thunder' weapon training deployment exercise at Zaragoza AB in Spain.

Above: F-16 Fighting Falcon multi-role fighters of the 8th Tactical Fighter Wing stand by on the flight line at Kunsan AB in South Korea during Exercise 'Team Spirit '86'.

commands for the most effective and economic deflection of the control surfaces. These latter comprise a powerful rudder, slab tailplane halves and full-span flaperons, the last serving as flaps and ailerons. The flaperons are linked by an automatically scheduled system with the full-span flaps to create what is in effect a variable-camber wing. The leading edges of the wings sweep forward to a point just behind the radome in large leading-edge root extensions that create the strong vortices which improve handling and controllability at high angles of attack.

Finally, the pilot is accommodated in a semi-reclining seat that improves his ability to sustain the higher g loads possible with the Fighting Falcon. This semi-reclined seat also allows the cockpit to be made shallower than would otherwise have been the case, but its high positioning under a blown and basically frameless canopy gives the pilot superb fields of vision.

Both engine types are versatile, powerful, fuel economical, optimized for the exacting fighter role, and full of development potential to ensure that the Fighting Falcon's performance is not compromised by the additional weapons and equipment that inevitably accrue to the basic design during any warplane's career. The engine is located in the rear fuselage, with structural beams extending from the central fuselage on each side of it to support the tailplane halves. This allows the engine to be changed easily. The engine is aspirated via a ventral inlet under cockpit, a position that ensures a good air supply to the engine, even at high angles of attack, and offers no impediments to the pilot's fields of vision.

Together with the 'fly-by-wire' system that provides superb handling combined with exceptional agility, the main electronic feature of the Fighting Falcon is the APG-66 radar. This was designed in 1975 as the most powerful equipment that could be produced without the need for liquid cooling. In common with other modern fighter radars, the APG-66 is of the pulse-Doppler type with the ability to look down toward the ground without the clutter problems encountered by older equipment, in which the target echo is swamped by returns from the ground. Range scales are provided to 11.5, 23, 46 and 92 miles (18.5, 37, 74 and 148km). The radar has 14 modes, some of them associated with frequency agility to avoid the worst effects of jamming, and all those essential for air combat are controlled by thumb-operated buttons on the throttle and sidestick controller, the two main controls in the HOTAS cockpit. The most important air-to-air mode is Downlook, which provides detection of head-on fighter sized targets at a range of 34.5 miles (55.5km) and gives a clutter-free display even when the targets are at treetop height. The other main air-to-air modes are Uplock, Dogfight, Radar Cursor, Designate, and Return to Search.

In the F-16C, the radar is the APG-68. This is an updated, improved and more versatile development of the APG-66 with a programmable signal processor. The new equipment weighs 337lb (153kg) compared with the APG-66's 296.5lb (134.5kg), but offers a maximum search range of 184 miles (296km) compared with the APG-66's theoretical limit of 92 miles (148km). The APG-68 radar has more than 22 different air-to-air and air-to-ground operating modes. The air-to-air modes include Range-while-search, Track-while-scan (of up to 10 targets), Search and Cued track-while-scan, Look-up search, Raid clutter assessment, and Multiple auto-acquisition air combat.

Above: An F-16 of the 8th TFW releases a decoy flare against heat-seeking missiles during 'Team Spirit '86'.
Left: The versatile radar carried in the F-16A/B is the Westinghouse APG-66 equipment, which is extremely reliable.

It is also worth noting at this stage that the air-to-ground modes include Real beam mapping with Doppler beam sharpening and scan freeze, Sea surface search, Beacon homing, Ground moving target indication and tracking, Fixed-target tracking, Terrain following, and Terrain avoidance.

Apart from the head-down displays in the cockpit, the pilot's most important display is the GEC (Marconi) head-up display inside the windscreen. In the F-16C this is the wider-angle type, and both variants allow the presentation of vital flight and tactical symbology. Thus the data are presented in the pilot's primary line of sight, and as the data are focused at infinity the pilot does not need to refocus his eyes between the HUD and the outside world. As a result, the pilot can concentrate on the tactical task with his eyes looking out of the cockpit and his hands on the throttle and stick.

The Fighting Falcon was designed as a tactical fighter, and is therefore fitted with a greater number of hardpoints than a dedicated air superiority fighter such as the Eagle, which has five hardpoints (one under the fuselage and two under each wing) in addition to the four positions on the lower sides of the engine trunks for medium-range air-to-air missiles.

The Fighting Falcon has nine hardpoints. These comprise a centreline unit under the fuselage (rated 2,200lb (1,000kg)), three under each wing (rated from inner to outer at 4,500lb (2,000kg), 3,500lb (1,600kg) and 700lb (300kg)), and one at each wingtip (rated at 425lb (193kg) and intended solely for the carriage of an AIM-9 Sidewinder short-range air-to-air

retirement of the Convair F-106A Delta Dart and McDonnell Douglas F-4C/D/E Phantom II from the air superiority role, which left a potential shortfall in the defence of the continental United States. The adaptation has proved comparatively simple, and now allows a slightly different but very valuable operational role for some of those Fighting Falcons based permanently in the United States, where a ground-attack capability is useful only for training rather than actual operations.

The conversion was undertaken in concert with the Operational Capabilities Upgrade programme, and in addition to the wiring for the Sparrow missile features the necessary continuous-wave illuminator to the APG-66. Other modifications are the receiver for the Global Positioning system (an advanced and highly accurate position-fixing system based on data broadcast by special satellites) and revision of the radar with the data-link required for use of the AIM-120 AMRAAM. This last is to replace the Sparrow as the Fighting Falcon's main medium-range weapon, and full provision is made for the weapon during production of the F-16C model of the Fighting Falcon.

Below: As this F-16A of the 50th TFW over Germany reveals, the Fighting Falcon was clearly designed for performance combined with agility rather than for outright flight performance.

Above: An F-16C shows off its armament of two AIM-120A AMRAAM and two AIM-9 Sidewinder air-to-air missiles.
Left: A 33rd TFS F-16 is seen on a Jordanian airfield.

missile). This gives the Fighting Falcon a theoretical payload limit of 20,450lb (9,276kg), though the carriage of this load imposes a manoeuvre limit of 5.5g. Full 9-g manoeuvre loads are possible if the payload is limited to 11,950lb (5,420kg), which is still a very respectable weight of ordnance or other external loads.

Such loads are required only for the ground-attack role. The air-to-air load is considerably lighter, and comprises two basic fits used in combination with the inbuilt M61A1 Vulcan cannon. This is installed with its muzzle in the upper surface of the port leading-edge root extension and fed with 515 rounds of ammunition from a magazine in the starboard side of the central fuselage just behind the forward integral fuselage fuel tank. The Vulcan is complemented in the Fighting Falcon's dogfighting role by two examples of the Sidewinder, and in the longer-range interception role by two examples of the AIM-7 Sparrow carried on the outermost underwing hardpoints.

With just two Sidewinders in addition to the Vulcan, the Fighting Falcon is the world's best dogfighter. Sparrows are in fact carried only by 270 Fighting Falcons revised from F-16A single-seaters and F-16B two-seaters to the F-16(ADF) standard for the air superiority role in the continental United States. The Fighting Falcon was not in fact planned with this role in mind, but the conversion was made desirable by the

STRIKE
Ground and Maritime Attack

The winning and retention of air superiority is the wholly essential concomitant of all other types of air operations, especially at the tactical level of offensive operations. In modern war, such tactical operations come under the overall heading of attack against surface targets. There are many subdivisions of attack, but the most important distinctions are between use of nuclear weapons (strike) and non-nuclear weapons (conventional attack), and operations behind the battlefield (interdiction) and over the battlefield (ground attack and, when integrated with the fire and movement of friendly ground forces, close air support).

As noted in the previous chapter, the General Dynamics F-16 Fighting Falcon is the most important warplane in the inventory of American tactical warplanes. Thus the Fighting Falcon's essentially secondary air superiority role is overshadowed by its two primary roles, which are counter-air and close air support operations.

Counter-air operations are the battlefield counterpart of air superiority, and involve the same tactics and weapons in the defensive and offensive task of defeating enemy air power. This demands that the enemy be prevented from using his air power to interfere with the conduct of tactical and surface operations of either an offensive or defensive nature. This is in fact the task for which the Fighting Falcon was primarily conceived, for its agility, radar, and comparatively light load of air-to-air weapons and all essentials for the hectic type of air-combat manoeuvring typical of counter-air operations. Such operations place great emphasis on dogfighting ability with short-range sensors and weapons, while the air superiority

Previous page: The A-10A reaches only medium altitude in transit flights where fuel economy is of prime importance. Below: An F-16 manoeuvres to take on fuel from a KC-135A.

role is better performed by larger and less agile fighters that carry longer-range sensors and a heavier weapon load of longer-range missiles. Inevitably there is a considerable measure of overlap between the two tasks, but while the major requirements of the air superiority role are nicely epitomized by the McDonnell Douglas F-15 Eagle, those of the counter-air role are beautifully characterized by the F-16.

Such is the versatility of the Fighting Falcon, however, that it is also a first-rate attack platform. Mention has been made in the previous chapter of the Fighting Falcon's very useful warload capability, and also of the air-to-ground modes of its main radar for target acquisition as well as navigation. This radar navigation facility also allows the F-16 to fly at very low altitudes at high speed without hitting the ground. Such performance is absolutely essential in modern warfare, where the best defence against radar-controlled anti-aircraft artillery and tactical surface-to-air missiles is a single pass over the target after a low-level approach masked by terrain features.

Such approaches are also aided by optional sensors such as the LANTIRN pod system, which uses infra-red and radar sensors to provide all-weather day/night navigation capability together with excellent acquisition of targets shielded from optical acquisition by the weather or haze.

The Fighting Falcon can carry weapons such as rocket-launcher pods, submunition dispensers for the strewing of anti-tank and anti-personnel mines, free-fall and retarded 'dumb' bombs, and cannon pods for direct attacks on ground targets. The type's capabilities are best exploited, however, with stand-off weapons that permit attacks of pinpoint accuracy without the need to fly over the target. Such weapons include the 'Paveway' family of laser-guided glide bombs, the GBU-15 and AGM-130 series of optronically guided glide bombs,

Above: An A-10A in typical operating conditions.

and the AGM-65 Maverick air-to-surface missile. This last can be carried in triplets on the innermost underwing hardpoints, and is used by the USAF in variants such as the 463lb (210kg) AGM-65A, AGM-65B with a 125lb (56.7kg) warhead and imaging TV guidance, the 485lb (220kg) AGM-65D with the same warhead and imaging infra-red guidance, the 667lb (303kg) AGM-65E with a 300lb (136kg) warhead and semi-active laser guidance, and the 670lb (304kg) AGM-65G with a 300lb (136kg) warhead and imaging infra-red guidance.

Below the Fighting Falcon's counter-air operations and beside its close air support activities is a particular subdivision, the anti-tank role. This involved the blunting of the enemy's armoured spearheads, and here the USAF's most important asset is the ungainly but highly impressive Fairchild Republic A-10A Thunderbolt II, known to its pilots as the 'Warthog'. The service currently operates more than 640 of the type, though plans are now afoot for this firmly subsonic type to be replaced by a supersonic platform, the planned A-16 version of the Fighting Falcon.

The USAFE's main operator of the Thunderbolt II is the 81st Tactical Fighter Wing, which is based at RAF Bentwaters and RAF Woodbridge in the English county of Suffolk. Bentwaters and Woodbridge are only the administrative and maintenance bases for the 81st TFW's 100 or more aircraft, which deploy to FOLs (Forward Operating Locations) in western Germany as soon as crisis threatens. Speed is of the essence in such a situation, and while the A-10As fly to their forward bases, their ground crews and other support personnel are ferried to Germany in Lockheed C-130 Hercules tactical transports.

The FOLs have considerable supplies of fuel and ordnance, and possess adequate facilities for first-line maintenance; however, any plane needing major work has to return to the UK. The current infrastructure of each FOL means that it is fully operational as soon as the A-10s arrive. As a result, each of the FOLs is a prime target for immediate attack by the enemy's interdictors, but the A-10A's semi-STOL capability means that 1,300 yards (1,190m) of undamaged runway are sufficient for full-load operations. If the FOL is destroyed as an operating base, there exist contingency plans for the A-10As to disperse into the surrounding countryside, where stretches of Autobahn and other straight roads can be pressed into emergency service as runways, with helicopters bringing in logistic equipment as well as fuel and ordnance.

The task of the A-10As permanently stationed in Europe is that of a 'fire brigade' force to check the enemy's advance, and so buy time for stronger US forces to arrive from the continental USA. Earmarked for movement in the first wave of these reinforcements are about 500 A-10As, mainly from the 23rd and 354th TFWs of Tactical Air Command, the 442nd and 917th TFWs of the Air Force Reserve, and the 128th and 174th TFWs of the Air National Guard supported by the 103rd, 104th and 175th Fighter Groups of the ANG. Other A-10As are operated by the Pacific Air Forces in South Korea.

Each sortie begins with a briefing in which the pilots receive a general assessment of the overall situation, and then information about the type of mission to be flown. If a set target is involved, the pilots are informed about ingress, weapons, tactics, and egress. All the aspects of the mission are discussed, including routes, diversion or emergency airfields, and districts that offer a particular threat. With their briefing complete, the pilots move to the duty desk, where they are assigned their aircraft. Then comes the important suiting-up procedure. In wartime, CBR (Chemical, Biological and Radiological) are always worn, even though this severely curtails the pilots' mobility and dexterity.

Meanwhile, in the 'snake pit' the ground crews have been preparing the A-10As for their mission. The fuel tanks are topped up. The magazine for the GAU-8/A Avenger seven-barrel rotary cannon is filled with its 1,174 rounds of 30mm ammunition, each projectile containing a high-density penetrator of depleted uranium that burns brightly once fired and therefore has great incendiary as well as kinetic effect on the target. The 11 hardpoints under the straight wings are loaded with ordnance, generally free-fall bombs and two triple clusters of AGM-65 Maverick air-to-surface missiles.

All these preparations are completed as the pilots are driven to their aircraft, where the crew chiefs are waiting. The pilot and crew chief for each aircraft complete a walk-round inspection together, checking the tyres, control surfaces, airframe, and external weapons load. The pilot then signs for the plane, and climbs into the cockpit. Here he straps himself into the ejector seat, connects himself into the oxygen system, and starts the vital pre-flight checks.

The auxiliary power unit is started, and this supplies the electrical power that allows the pilot to align the all-

Right: The A-10A is supported by a special loader to ensure fast and accurate filling of the large ammunition tank.
Below: A-10As take off for air-to-ground gunnery training.

Above: An A-10A of the 91st TFS practises ground-attack manoeuvres with friendly armour in Exercise 'Busy Brewer'.

important inertial navigation system. Though conceived as a low-cost attacker without 'frills', the A-10A has increased in capability and complexity over the years, and after he has checked the three radio equipments, the pilot then confirms that his head-up display and other elements of the advanced nav/attack system are working properly.

A radio call to the tower elicits permission for engine start, and once the two turbofans have been fired up the APU is shut down. There remains only a check for free movement of the control surfaces, and once the crew chief has confirmed by the plug-in intercom system that these are all moving properly, he disconnects himself and pulls away the chocks.

The A-10As operate in flights of two or four, and on the command to taxi the aircraft move from their dispersal areas in the right tactical formation, and move to the arming area. Here armourers swarm over the A-10As, fusing weapons and removing their safety pins. With their weapons 'live', each flight is cleared to move onto the runway and take-off.

As soon as it has cleared the airfield, each flight moves into combat formation and climbs to transit altitude. The combat formation is usually a 'swan' or 'card', which allow the aircraft to cover each other and thus provide security against the possibility of being bounced by enemy fighters.

As they approach the battlefield, the 'Warthogs' drop down to treetop height and start the crunch part of the mission, and any four-plane flight splits into two pairs, each comprising a leader and wingman. The attack is usually made by the lead pair, with the back-up pair loitering to the rear of the battle front. As soon as the lead pair has made its attack, the back-up pair moves forward, this 'cab rank' system by several flights ensuring that the ground forces receive constant cover with a pair of A-10As on call all the time.

Over the battlefield, the A-10As almost always operate under the command of an FAC (Forward Air Controller), who undertakes the dual tasks of directing them onto their targets and warning them of enemy defences as well as the presence of any friendly forces. These all-important FACs operate on the ground, either in the front line or even as single units ahead of the troops, or in light helicopters such as the Bell OH-58 Kiowa. As a rule, the A-10A pilot prefers to be directed by an airborne FAC, for the simple reason that the two men are seeing possible targets and threats in the same way. It is rare for A-10As to communicate directly with the ground forces, for it requires a trained intermediary such as the FAC to 'translate' the requirements of the ground forces into the type of information that can instantly be assimilated by the A-10A pilot.

As it moves into the attack, the A-10A drops to very low level and weaves as it flies. Exactly how low the plane can get depends on factors such as the terrain, weather, pilot experience, and nature of the enemy's defences. Over the comparatively flat country of northern Europe, hedge-hopping flight is the norm, while in the hillier country of southern Europe a pilot generally opts to skim over ridges and fly down valleys, so weaving his way through the twists and turns of the terrain. The more experienced he is, the more capable each pilot feels of flying at very low level, and as pilots train regularly over the areas in which they may have to fight, they come to know the area almost to the level of every copse, rocky outcrop, pylon, and farm house.

On receiving the attack call from his FAC, the A-10A pilot approaches the front line at the lowest possible level, jinking all the while to present the hardest possible target to the enemy's air defences. At a set distance from the target (a range determined by the weather and the type of weapons being used), the pilot pulls up sharply to a few hundred feet, acquires the target visually in his head-up display, aims, and

fires. In this stable dive from modest height, the A-10A is at its most vulnerable, so as soon as the gun has been fired or the other weapons released, the pilot banks steeply away from the target and dives as sharply as possible for the ground, the object being to get the cover of a ridge or copse between the enemy and the A-10A.

Though its low speed and considerable agility make it better able to deal with adverse conditions at low level than higher-performance types, the A-10A lacks all-weather capability and may under the most difficult of conditions be forced to suspend operations.

Being slow and fairly large, the A-10A has long aroused suspicions of vulnerability to the mobile anti-aircraft artillery and surface-to-air missiles that defend the armoured and mechanised formations that are the Thunderbolt II's intended prey. The type uses its manoeuvrability to mask its approach via terrain features and woods, possesses electronic defences in the form of the ALE-37 chaff dispenser and jammer pods such as the ALQ-119 and ALQ-131 units, and its engines, which are located in positions flanking the fuselage, are partially shielded by the wings and tail unit against ground-launched missiles with infra-red guidance. If hit, the A-10A relies on its redundant structural and system features to survive, with the pilot and other essential singleton systems protected by the titanium armour 'bath' that forms the structural core of the forward fuselage.

A-10A units are often teamed with helicopters to create the Joint Air Attack Team. The helicopter generally used in the JAAT is the Bell AH-1 HueyCobra, one of the US Army's mainstays. This is a radical development of the UH-1 Iroquois utility helicopter (universally known as the 'Huey') with greater power, a very slim fuselage tailored to the width of the two crew members seated in tandem on vertically staggered seats, and the armament and sensors for the close air support and attack roles.

The AH-1 was developed to meet an army requirement of the Vietnam War for an escort helicopter also able to undertake the fire-support role troops landed from the escorted UH-1s. The Model 209 prototype first flew in September 1965, and then entered production as the AH-1G. The HueyCobra has undergone very extensive

Above: An A-10A is engulfed in gun gases as it fires its 30-mm cannon, the world's most powerful air-to-surface gun.

development, in the process emerging as a potent tank killer, and the definitive version is the AH-1S with the 1,800shp Avco Lycoming T53-L-703 turboshaft. This carries a traversing chin turret, controlled by the gunner and armed with one M197 three-barrel 20mm cannon, and stub wings whose four hardpoints generally carry two launchers for 2.75 in rockets and two quadruple launchers for the BGM-71 TOW heavyweight anti-tank missile. This last is

Above: Missile-carrying AH-1S HueyCobras line up for take-off at Norton AFB in California during 'Gallant Eagle '86'.

command-guided over trailing wires by the gunner, who is equipped with the excellent M65 TOW sight.

The US Army has more than 900 HueyCobras, and the AH-1S model is now used in four variants produced as the Modified AH-1S, Production AH-1S, Up-gun AH-1S and Modernized AH-1S but known in service as the AH-1S, AH-1P, AH-1E and AH-1F respectively.

In the JAAT, the standard tactic is for the Thunderbolt IIs to

engage the target formation's anti-aircraft defences (in the Soviet tank division the ZSU-23-4 tracked vehicle with four radar-controlled 23mm cannon, and various types of surface-to-air missile launcher vehicles) and so allow the HueyCobras a comparatively free run against the tanks and armoured personnel carriers. Only after they have suppressed the defensive vehicles do the Thunderbolt IIs join the HueyCobras in attacking the armoured vehicles. To avoid collisions, the fixed-wing aircraft operate above the tree tops and the rotary-wing helicopters below them.

The US Marine Corps also operates a SeaCobra version of

Left: A US Army mechanic services an AH-1G as two more HueyCobras of the same type fly overhead.

Below: The pilot and gunner of an AH-1 SeaCobra discuss their mission before take-off in a Norwegian deployment.

the HueyCobra in the close air support and anti-tank roles. Intended for operation from amphibious warfare vessels lying offshore before moving onto beach-head strips, this model has to fly over water, perhaps with battle damage, and thus requires greater flight reliability. It is therefore fitted with a coupled twin-turbine powerplant. In the initial AH-1J this was the 1,800shp Pratt & Whitney Canada T400-CP-400, which was upgraded to the 2,050shp T400-WV-402 in the AH-1T Improved SeaCobra. In the definitive AH-1W SuperCobra, this coupled powerplant has been replaced by two General Electric T700-GE-401 turboshafts driving through a combining gearbox to deliver a maximum of 3,250shp. The marines currently field 165 of these helicopters, which have advanced sensors and the choice of the AGM-114 Hellfire anti-tank missile with semi-active laser guidance instead of the wire-guided BGM-71 TOW.

The US Army's other main battlefield helicopter is the McDonnell Douglas AH-64A Apache, of which slightly more than 800 are to be procured. This is the world's most powerful battlefield helicopter, and was first flown in September 1975 after development by Hughes Helicopters, which was later bought by McDonnell Douglas. Powered by two 1,696shp General Electric T700-GE-701 turboshafts, the Apache has good performance and is well protected by armour, design features, and active/passive defensive electronics. The type has very advanced sensors for all-weather day and night flight, target acquisition and target designation.

The armament of the Apache comprises a 30mm cannon and disposable stores carried on four hardpoints under the stub wings. The cannon is of the single-barrel type, located in a training and elevating mounting under the fuselage, under control of the gunner's helmet-controlled sighting system, for use in suppressing enemy ground fire and destroying both soft-skinned and light armoured vehicles. The hardpoints can carry a 3,880lb (1,760kg) load, and this generally comprises four four-round launchers for Hellfire missiles, or four 19-tube rocket-launcher pods, or two launchers of each type. In common with other American battlefield helicopters, the Apache is now faced with the probability of meeting enemy helicopters with anti-helicopter weapons, and as a defensive measure is therefore being provided with the AIM-92A short-range air-to-air version of the FIM-92A Stinger man-portable surface-to-air missile.

Below: The AH-64A Apache has a very purposeful appearance with its underfuselage cannon and underwing stores.

Above: This AV-8B Harrier II is seen with the formidable load of 16 1,000-lb bombs under the fuselage and wings.

For obvious operational reasons, US Naval Aviation has no requirement for an equivalent to the A-10A. For equally obvious reasons, the air arm of the US Marine Corps does possess such a need, for it is faced with the task of providing close air support for ground forces in an amphibious beach-head. Anti-tank capability is provided in this scenario by the SeaCobra series of helicopters, which can operate from cleared areas within the beach-head if necessary, but this is seldom possible with conventional fixed wing aircraft.

The obvious solution was the STOVL warplane of the type pioneered by a British warplane, the Hawker Siddeley (later British Aerospace) Harrier. An Americanized version of the definitive Harrier GR.Mk 3 version of this innovative close air support fighter was adopted by the US Marine Corps as the AV-8A Harrier with simplified and less capable electronics, and some aircraft were later upgraded to AV-8C standard. Both these models have been replaced by an altogether more capable machine of the same basic type, namely the McDonnell Douglas/British Aerospace AV-8B Harrier II.

The American requirement is for 328 of these aircraft (including TAV-8B combat-capable two-seat trainers) to serve with eight operational squadrons. The AV-8B entered service in October 1983 and, after replacing the AV-8A and AV-8C, is now supplanting the McDonnell Douglas A-4M Skyhawk II. This is the last first-line version of the legendary 'bantam bomber' left in moderately large-scale American service, where 130 or more examples still fly in the light attack role.

As its designation implies, the Harrier II is a radical development of the Harrier by BAe's American licensee with support from the British parent company, and was produced to meet the specific needs of the US Marine Corps (close air support in the beach-head lodgement) though the type has

also been bought with a number of different features for the Royal Air Force. The Harrier II is modelled closely on the Harrier in overall concept and configuration, but almost every part of the airframe has been redesigned to improve lift, reduce weight or curtail maintenance requirements.

The most obvious and important major new component is the wing, which is larger yet lighter than that of the Harrier. The wing is a single-piece structure mainly of graphite/epoxy composite construction with a deeper supercritical aerofoil section, increased span and area, and reduced sweep. The wing provides considerably more lift at all speeds, increases internal fuel capacity by some 50 per cent, and provides greater area for lift as well as the accommodation of underwing hardpoints, which are increased in number to six from the Harrier's four. Together with the underfuselage hardpoint, this increases the Harrier II's disposable warload to 17,000lb (7,710kg) or more from the 8,000lb (3,630kg) of the Harrier.

Though British Aerospace designed the curved leading-edge root extensions that provide greater turn rate and thereby improve dogfighting capability, the basic wing was a McDonnell Douglas responsibility. Other American features on the wing are the revised geometry and the large slotted flaps that are lowered for better vertical lift, while other McDonnell Douglas contributions include the square-cut extended nozzles that combine with lowered flaps and drooped ailerons to provide a STOL lift gain of 6,700lb (3,040kg), larger air inlets for the 21,450lb (9,730kg) thrust Rolls-Royce F402-RR-406A (or from 1990 the 25,000lb (11,340kg) thrust F402-RR-408) vectored-thrust turbofan, better lift-improvement devices under the fuselage to trap exhaust gases and thereby further enhance vertical lift, and a generally beefed-up structure. Another major revision is the raised cockpit: this offers the pilot considerably superior fields of vision, while its modern ergonomic design includes HOTAS controls and modern instrumentation including a head-down display in addition to the standard head-up display.

The Harrier II is also fitted with modern operational electronics centred on an integrated nav/attack system. The single most important item is the ASB-19(V)2 Angle-Rate Bombing Set. This is mounted in the nose of the Harrier II, and comprises a TV/laser target seeker and tracker that allows the pilot to identify and acquire a target that is then attacked with weapons released automatically regardless of the pilot's chosen approach angle and speed. The ARBS also allows acquisition of a target illuminated by a friendly laser (airborne or ground-based) for first-pass attack with laser-guided weapons for an equally high probability of success.

The Harrier II was not conceived as a dogfighter, but once it has unloaded its disposable weapon load is no mean performer in such combat. In this flight regime, the type possesses comparatively low wing loading and this offers considerable advantages in manoeuvrability over fighters with higher wing loadings. The root extensions make a significant contribution to this agility. Another factor that enhances the Harrier II's agility is the possibility of VIFFing (Vectoring In Forward Flight), a technique pioneered by the pilots of the US Marine Corps. This involves use of the Harrier II's thrust-vectoring nozzles in wingborne rather than thrust-borne flight for rapid deceleration or for the generation of inward-acting thrust during the turn to decrease turn radius by a marked degree. In these circumstances, the Harrier II should prove itself well able to meet even modern fighters under equal if not advantageous terms in close-range encounters in the way that the Royal Navy's Sea Harrier FRS.Mk 1 presaged in the Falklands War of 1982.

The Harrier II is still a young design full of development potential. In the short term, the US Marine Corps' most pressing requirement is for a version capable of night and all-

Below: The nature of the typical amphibious assault can be deduced from this illustration of two AV-8B Harrier II close support aircraft on the assault ship Belleau Wood.

Above: Among the AV-8B Harrier II's many tactically useful attributes is the ability for easy dispersal into sheltered areas that permit the type to conduct unimpeded operations.

Below: An F-4E and an F-4G 'Wild Weasel' team of the 561st TFS. Both machines carry ALQ-119 ECM pods, and the F-4G has two AGM-45, one AGM-65 and one AGM-78 missiles.

weather attack. From September 1989, 156 Harrier IIs are being delivered with provision for an equipment package derived from that introduced on the F/A-18D two-seat version of the F/A-18C Hornet, and this package is due for retrofit to older aircraft. The package includes a fixed forward-looking infra-red sensor whose imagery is displayed on the pilot's head-up display, Cat's Eye night vision goggles for the pilot, and a digital moving map display. The next step is the installation of nose radar, and it is planned that the last 40 aircraft will be delivered in this Harrier II Plus standard with APG-65 radar. It is planned that the radar should be retrofitted to the older aircraft as the second part of the programme whose first part is the retrofit of the optronic night-attack package.

For self-defence, the Harrier II can carry two or four AIM-9 Sidewinder air-to-air missiles on the two outer pairs of hardpoints, and has powerful gun armament in the form of its GAU-12/U Equalizer cannon. This system is accommodated in the two underfuselage fairings that are an important part of the lift-improvement system. The port fairing carries the 25mm five-barrel gun (of the externally powered rotary type) and the starboard fairing 300 rounds of ammunition fed to the cannon through the shallow bridge connecting the rear part of the two main fairings.

It is clear from assessment of the tasks and capabilities of the above attack aircraft that the single factor that most severely limits ground-attack operations is not counter-air fighters but the enemy's battlefield anti-aircraft defence system. Modern anti-aircraft weapons are a potentially decisive battlefield factor, and generally comprise armoured vehicles fitted with fast-firing multiple cannon and quick-reaction surface-to-air missiles. Both types have radar and/or optronic target acquisition and tracking sensors feeding data to advanced computerized fire-control systems, and can decimate groups of attacking aircraft.

The elimination of these anti-aircraft systems is the task of the 'Wild Weasel' aircraft, of which the most important is the McDonnell Douglas F-4G Phantom II, one of the last Phantom II variants to possess a truly front-line role in the inventory of the American armed forces. The F-4G is a conversion of the F-4E, and more than 100 are currently in service with the 37th Tactical Fighter Wing at George Air Force Base in California for training and deployment as required, the 3rd TFW at Clark Air Base in the Philippines for all 'Wild Weasel' work in the Far East, and the 52nd TFW at Spangdahlem Air Base in Germany for operations in Europe.

The 'Wild Weasel' task is generally flown by two pairs of aircraft, each pair comprising one F-4G and one F-4E, though extra F-4Es are added to this basic unit if the situation demands. The USAF still operates more than 400 examples of the F-4E, some of them in the secondary air defence role but most for the ground-attack task, which includes co-operation with F-4Gs in the 'Wild Weasel' defence-suppression role.

The F-4E carries a Vulcan six-barrel cannon in the lower nose, but in the F-4G conversion this is replaced by part of the APR-38 passive detection system that forms the core of this variant's capability. The system has many antennae for the detection of electromagnetic radiation from enemy radars. These signals are then classified, identified, and localized by the system's computer, which also memorizes the location of the emitting radar so that it can be attacked even if it shuts down. The resulting data are displayed to the electronic warfare officer in the F-4G's rear seat, whose display lists all the detected radars by type, notes the 15 most threatening,

Above: This 'Wild Weasel' team of the 561st TFS is equipped with ALQ-119 ECM pods and AGM-45 Shrike missiles, while the F-4G also has an AGM-78 Standard ARM under the port wing.

and encloses that offering the highest threat in a triangular symbol.

The pairs of aircraft make for their positions just on the friendly side of the front line at low altitude, generally about 500ft (150m), and then adopt an orbital flight pattern in the shadow of a masking terrain feature. The next part of the mission requires the F-4G to undertake a dangerous 'coat trailing' climb into the detection envelope of the radars associated with surface-to-air missile systems such as the SA-6 'Gainful', SA-8 'Gecko' and SA-11 'Gadfly'. The object here is to become vulnerable sufficiently long for the enemy's radars to acquire the F-4G and thereby provide the APR-38 system with the radar energy it needs to locate the radars and their position, but not long enough for the enemy to launch a surface-to-air missile. As the F4-G pops up from behind masking terrain to secure this information, the F-4E accompanying it remains under cover.

The next task is the destruction of the selected radar or radars by the F-4G and its F-4E partner. The F-4G carries two examples of the AGM-88 HARM (High-speed Anti-Radiation Missile), whose seeker receives data directly from the APR-38 system. Weighing 796lb (361kg) in its basic AGM-88A form, the HARM is then fired. The missile homes on the source of radar energy or, if the radar shuts down, on its last known position, at more than Mach 3. The kinetic energy of the missile is sufficient to cause very considerable damage on its own, but the AGM-88A also possesses a potent 145lb (66kg) warhead with a laser-activated proximity fuse.

The F-4G can also carry the older and less effective AGM-45 Shrike, a 390lb (180kg) weapon with a 145lb (66kg) warhead fitted with proximity and impact fuses. The Shrike carries one of at least 13 narrow-band seekers that must be installed before take-off, and can only be used if an emitter of the right frequency is encountered. The Shrike also lacks a memory, so if the target emitter shuts down the missile goes ballistic.

This is also the missile carried by the F-4E, whose two crewmen receive information by voice communications or data-link. In addition to the Shrike, the F-4E carries cluster bombs and/or 250lb (110kg) free-fall or retarded bombs. Such an attack, usually made by the two aircraft together so that the F-4G can provide targeting data, is more dangerous than a stand-off missile attack, but can saturate the target area with up to 18 bombs. Virtually no radar could survive an accurately delivered attack of this type, in which the blast of the bombs is supplemented by a devastating sheet of high-

speed metal fragments created out of the bursting bomb casings.

The other major type upon which the USAF can call is the A-7D. There are still some 380 or more (including the A-7K two-seat combat trainer model) of this type in service, and these are operated by 13 tactical fighter squadrons of the Air National Guard. The A-7 was developed for the US Navy as a carrierborne medium attack platform, and first flew in September 1965 after very rapid development as a subsonic type derived aerodynamically from the F-8 Crusader supersonic fighter. The type entered service during October 1966 as the A-7A Corsair II with the 11,350lb (5,150kg) thrust Pratt & Whitney TF30-P-6 turbofan, and proved very successful.

The type was then adopted for the USAF, whose version has no name. This A-7D introduced the M61A1 six-barrel cannon with 1,032 rounds of ammunition (in place of the naval model's two single-barrel 20mm cannon with 250 rounds per gun), the 14,500lb (6,580kg) Allison TF41-A-1 turbofan (a licensed version of a British engine, the Rolls-Royce Spey), and a considerably more advanced all-weather nav/attack system. This last includes multi-mode radar (with 10 operating modes including terrain following), an inertial navigation, a head-up display, and a versatile mission computer for navigation, targeting and weapon release.

Once in service, the A-7Ds were retrofitted with automatic manoeuvring flaps for increased agility, and with the 'Pave Penny' tracker for acquisition of laser-illuminated targets. Still later, most aircraft were fitted with the LANA (Low-Altitude Night Attack) package, which uses an AAR-49 forward-looking infra-red sensor, pod-mounted under the

Above left: An 81st TFS F-4E releases 18 500-lb bombs.
Above: This A-7D of the 137th TFW carries at least one AIM-9 Sidewinder and an ALQ-131 ECM pod.

starboard wing, for a night capability using imagery displayed on a new wide-angle HUD.

The A-7D can carry a very diverse offensive load on eight hardpoints (one on each side of the fuselage used for self-defence air-to-air missiles, and three under each wing). The maximum warload is 15,000lb (6,800kg) of precision-guided weapons (including the whole range of USAF air-to-surface missiles and guided glide bombs), 'dumb' bombs of the free-fall or retarded types, cluster bombs, submunition dispensers and rocket-launcher pods.

One of the most important weapons carried by the A-7D, and indeed by most other American tactical warplanes, is the 'Rockeye' dispenser, which was developed by the US Naval Weapons Center as an anti-tank cluster bomb. The variant used by US Naval Aviation and the air arm of the US Marine Corps is the 'Rockeye' Cluster Bomb Mk 20 Mod 2. This weighs 490lb (220kg), and is a dispenser filled with 247 anti-tank bomblets weighing 334lb (151kg). Dropped from 500ft (150m) in a toss-bomb manoeuvre, the Mk 20 saturates a 3,333 sq yard (2,787m²) oval with its bomblets, each of which can destroy an armoured personnel carrier or disable a tank. The USAF version of this weapon is the CBU-59/B 'Rockeye II', which weighs 766lb (347kg) with its load of 717 anti-

Below left: These are A-7Ks of the 132nd TFW, Iowa ANG and 124th TFS, Arizona ANG en route to Japan for training.
Below: An A-7 of the 76th TFS releases 500-lb bombs.

Above: An A-7 on the ground at Elmendorf AFB during Air Force and Navy joint manoeuvres in the northern Pacific. Below: A-7E Corsair IIs on the flight deck of the Midway.

personnel and anti-*materiel* bomblets. A considerably improved version of the 'Rockeye II' is the ISCB-1, which uses the same dispenser casing filled with 160 electronically timed anti-tank submunitions and 65 dummy mines. The saturation area of this weapon is between 3,600 and 5,625 sq yards (3,010 and 4,703m²), and the presence of the dummy submunitions would considerably slow the enemy's clearance of the minefield created by the weapon.

This is only one of several dispenser weapons (or cluster bombs) carried by American tactical aircraft. Most are designed to hinder the enemy's armoured forces, or to channel them into preselected killing zones where they can be engaged by friendly tanks or tank-killing aircraft of the fixed- and rotary-wing types.

Other dispenser weapons are designed to deny the enemy use of his own airpower by cratering the runways or destroying aircraft in their hardened aircraft shelters. Typical of this species is the BLU-106/B Boosted Kinetic Energy Penetrator, which weighs 45lb (20kg) and can be carried in multiple by several dispenser weapons. Once released from its dispenser at low altitude, the BKEP releases a drogue parachute that pitches down the nose, whereupon the drogue is released and rocket motor ignited to accelerate the BKEP to a speed sufficient for it to penetrate the concrete runway pavement or hardened aircraft shelter before the 6.5lb (2.9kg) warhead is exploded, causing considerable heave and fracture damage.

Despite the electronic improvements made to the type, the A-7D is now considered obsolescent for use in a high-intensity war against an enemy with modern anti-aircraft weapons. Vought proposed to the USAF a radical A-7 Plus development with supersonic performance provided by a lengthened fuselage, leading-edge root extensions and more power from a General Electric F110 or Pratt & Whitney F100 turbofan. This proposal was evaluated in the form of two YA-7F prototypes, but in 1990 the service decided instead to adopt the A-16 dedicated attack derivative of the F-16 Fighting Falcon.

The Corsair II is still in valuable service with US Naval Aviation, which operates a number of two-seat training models in addition to 220 or more of the definitive A-7E model. The Corsair II is being supplanted by the McDonnell Douglas F/A-18 Hornet, but will remain an important carrierborne asset until well into the 1990s.

The current naval version is the A-7E, which is essentially the naval counterpart of the A-7D with the same nav/attack system, armament arrangement, and basic engine in the form of the 15,000lb (6,800kg) thrust TF41-A-2. From 1978 the service adopted the AAR-42 forward-looking infra-red pod (carried on the innermost hardpoint under the starboard wing) to provide adverse-weather attack capability. Financial considerations limited procurement to just 91 of these important pods, so pod-fitted aircraft serve as leaders for other A-7Es carrying just weapons on their hardpoints.

Each of US Naval Aviation's carrier air wings includes three attack squadrons in its overall strength. Two of these are light/medium attack squadrons equipped with the Corsair II or the F/A-18 Hornet, and the third is a medium attack squadron equipped with the Grumman A-6E/TRAM

Intruder. This is the most important 'bomb truck' in service with US Naval Aviation and the air arm of the US Marine Corps, which have respectively more than 250 and 75 of the type in service.

The service's need for the type was realized in the early 1950s. Despite the success of the diminutive Douglas A-4 Skyhawk light attacker, which has now disappeared from front-line naval service but remain in limited use as an 'aggressor' trainer, analysis of their experience in the Korean War persuaded the US Navy and US Marine Corps that they required an attack type able to carry and deliver heavy loads under all weather conditions. The firmly subsonic A-6 was the result. The type's forte is low flight under any and all weather conditions, by day and night, for the delivery of heavy warloads with pinpoint accuracy.

The US Navy's requirement was issued in 1956, and in the following year the G-128 design from Grumman (one of 11 proposals from eight companies) was accepted for initial hardware development as eight YA2F-1 prototypes. The type first flew in April 1960 with two 8,500lb (3,885kg) thrust Pratt & Whitney J52-P-6 turbojets and considerable internal fuel capacity for very good range. The type is notable for its adequate performance and its uncomplicated aerodynamics with only modestly swept flying surfaces and a broad fuselage accommodating the two crew members (pilot and bombardier-navigator) on side-by-side ejector seats.

There followed 484 examples of the A2F-1 initial model that was designated A-6A in 1962. Like later models, this had a substantial nose radome accommodating the antennae for the large APQ-92 search radar and small APQ-88 (later APQ-112) track radar, whose data were processed by the first digital computer to reach service in any warplane. This was the core of the Intruder's very advanced Digital Integrated Attack and Navigation Equipment, which also used inputs from Dopper navigation and inertial navigation systems to provide wholly exceptional accuracy of navigation and attack under all conditions.

There followed several variants in small numbers before the advent of the definitive A-6E model in 1972. This was produced by converting 192 A-6As as well as building new aircraft, and has the same 9,300lb (4,200kg) thrust J52-P-8B turbojets as later A-6As. Where the A-6E differs from the A-6A is in its all-important electronics, which are of the solid-state type to remove many of the reliability and maintenance problems that plagued the pioneering A-6A. The separate search and track radars of the A-6A were replaced by the single APQ-148 radar, later updated to the more capable APQ-156 to produce the current standard with moving target indication, terrain following and terrain avoidance capabilities. The type also introduced the improved Carrier Aircraft Inertial Navigation System and an automatic carrier landing system, and the cockpit was revised with the world's first head-down displays for flight data, navigation information and weapon-delivery cues.

Below: A plane director guides an A-6E/TRAM Intruder medium attack plane of VA-34 'Blue Blasters' onto one of the catapults on the flight deck of the carrier Saratoga.

Above: A-6Es of VA-34 reveal their elusive appearance during low-visibility operations in the Mediterranean.

The Intruder proved itself highly capable and adaptable during the Vietnam War, and experience in this conflict decided the US Naval Aviation to upgrade its A-6Es to A-6E/TRAM standard. This involved the installation under the nose of the AAS-33 Target Recognition and Attack Multi-sensor package in a trainable turret. The package adds to the Intruder a forward-looking infra-red sensor for improved navigation and target acquisition capabilities, and a laser for rangefinding, the designation of targets, and the acquisition of targets marked by other lasers. The first A-6E/TRAM flew in 1974, and the variant entered service in 1979.

Like earlier models, the A-6E/TRAM has five hardpoints (one under the fuselage and two under each wing) and can lift a maximum warload of 18,000lb (8,165kg). Earlier Intruders were limited to 'dumb' weapons, but the A-6E/TRAM has the capability to carry and launch fire-and-forget as well as laser-guided weapons. Fifty of the aircraft also have the ability to carry two AGM-84 Harpoon anti-ship missiles.

There were plans for improved A-6F and A-6G versions with turbofan power and more modern electronic systems, but both concepts were dropped in 1990. The Intruder is still a key element in US Naval Aviation's capabilities, however, and at least 178 aircraft are to be upgraded by the retrofit of improved electronics (head-up display, head-down displays, satellite navigation system, missile-approach warning system and towed active missile-decoy system) and a wing of composite construction, designed and built by Boeing.

In common with other American tactical aircraft, the Intruders operate in pairs. After catapult launch from their parent carrier, the two A-6E/TRAMs of any pair make for their target, transiting at the optimum altitude for fuel economy. As the two aircraft approach the enemy's coast, they drop down to the lowest possible altitude and so make it considerably more difficult for the enemy's radar to detect them. As they cross the coast, the two pilots separate their aircraft in a carefully pre-arranged plan to approach and hit their target from different headings, which further complicates the task facing the enemy's defence forces.

Flying at below 500ft (150m), or right down 'in the weeds' if possible, to provide the enemy radar with the smallest and most difficult to detect target, the bombardier-navigator soon receives on his screen indications from the ALR-45 radar warning receiver that the enemy radar is trying to pinpoint the position of the Intruder, which is now well on its way to the target. If it seems that the enemy radar is getting a lock on the Intruders, the bombardier-navigator can activate any or all of his machine's electronic countermeasures, which include the ALQ-41 or ALQ-100 deception jammers, the ALQ-126B deception jammer, and the ALE-29 chaff or ALE-40 chaff/flare dispenser.

Moving in toward the target at slightly more than 400mph (640km/h), the Intruder hugs the ground, its avionic systems adjusting the flight profile to take account of every rise or depression in the ground ahead of the aircraft. The FLIR sensor of the TRAM package allows the bombardier-navigator to acquire the target at long range on his vertical display

Above: Two A-6Es of VA-34 and one A-7E of VA-46 'Clansmen' of Carrier Air Wing 7 from the Dwight D. Eisenhower.

Below: Photographed from an A-6E, this is a KA-6D Intruder trailing its drogue for an inflight refuelling link-up.

indicator screen, and he then uses optical zoom to produce an enhanced and magnified image. Taking course instructions from the bombardier-navigator, the pilot directs his Intruder to the computer-selected Initial Point, about 10 miles from the target. The target is to be attacked with free-fall bombs, and the bombardier-navigator calls off the rapidly decreasing distance to the target he has now acquired in his optical sight.

The pilot has the option between a manual or automatic attack. In the manual mode, he presses the bomb-release button on top of his control column at the appropriate moment. In the automatic mode, he pulls the commit switch on the control column, and this authorizes the computer of the ASQ-133 nav/attack system to release the bombs at exactly the calculated point.

The use of 'smart' weapons involves the bombardier-navigator, who operates the TRAM package's laser to mark the target for a 'Paveway' series glide bomb, or alternatively to search for a target already illuminated by a friendly laser. Another option is to mark the target for the other Intruder of the tactical pair.

As its weapons fall away, the lightened Intruder bounds up and the pilot is free to take avoiding action. The pilot may have become concerned by the approach of anti-aircraft cannon fire (made visible by its occasional tracer rounds) during the approach to the target from the IP, but only now can he start to jink his Intruder. This is a good point to activate the ALE-29 or ALE -40 dispensers and so break the lock which the anti-aircraft artillery's radar may have on the Intruder, and indications by the ALR-50 missile-launch

Below: An FB-111A of Strategic Air Command's 715th BS on the flight line at Pease AFB, New Hampshire.

warning system may now confirm the crew in this decision.

The second Intruder attacks almost immediately after the first from a different direction, and the two attackers then depart the scene as they entered it, low and fast. Over the coast they climb once more to cruise altitude, in the process being 'deloused' by a machine such as the Grumman EA-6B Prowler to ensure that they are not being tracked by enemy fighters. If necessary, the aircraft take on fuel from a Grumman KA-6D Intruder 'buddy' refuelling tanker, and then return to their parent carrier and the inevitable debriefing. The TRAM package automatically records all images on its scope, and this helps to confirm that the right target was attacked and destroyed.

The Intruder can lift not only a considerable weight but also a great diversity of ordnance, including tactical-, operational- and strategic-level nuclear weapons. Combined with a radius of well over 500 miles (800km) under typical operating conditions, this allows the Intruder to strike at almost all types of target, thereby giving this elderly but still effective attacker a capability far beyond the merely tactical.

To this extent the Intruder is as much an interdictor at the strategic and operational levels as a conventional attack or nuclear strike platform at the operational and tactical levels. The Intruder thus has much in common with the USAF's primary interdictor, the General Dynamics F-111. There are currently some 380 of these variable-geometry aircraft in service. The two main variants of this fascinating type are the FB-111 strategic bomber, of which 60 are operational with the four squadrons of Strategic Air Command's 380th and 509th Bombardment Wings, and the other 320 or more with the 11 squadrons of Tactical Air Command's 20th, 27th, 48th and 366th Tactical Fighter Wings.

The F-111 is colloquially known as the 'Aardvark', and resulted from a politically imposed decision to produce a twin-turbofan warplane able to meet the USAF's requirement for a tactical strike fighter and the US Navy's specification for a fleet defence fighter with powerful radar and long-range missiles. The decision was based on the economic premise that considerable cost savings would result from large-scale manufacture of a single basic airframe and a single basic engine, but ignored the obvious fact that the USAF and US Navy requirements were in many ways incompatible. The first prototype flew in December 1964 after an extremely ambitious design programme that incorporated innovative features such as variable-geometry 'swing wings', extensive use of titanium in the structure, high-lift aerofoils, afterburning turbofan engines, and terrain-following radar.

The F-111B naval model with AWG-9 radar and AIM-54 Phoenix missiles was delayed by a host of problems, and even then was immensely overweight and therefore cancelled. (This led to the development of the Grumman F-14 Tomcat using the F-111B's powerplant, radar and armament). Greater success attended the land-based tactical strike fighter version, and after problems with electronic integration, higher than aniticipated drag and engine inlet had been addressed in a protracted development programme, the F-111A entered service in October 1967.

Even so, the F-111A's problems had not been fully resolved and the model had a disastrous operational debut in South-East Asia. Gradually the problems were eliminated, and production of the F-111 totalled 537 aircraft in six main variants. The type matured as an exceptional interdictor, and the two most important variants are those operated by the six squadrons of two wings within the US Air Forces in Europe organization. At RAF Upper Heyford the 20th TFW flies the F-111E, and at RAF Lakenheath the 48th TFW uses the F-111F. The slightly less capable F-111D is operational with two TAC wings based in the continental United States.

The pilot sits in the left-hand seat, with the weapons system

Below: An airman checks a rack of 500-lb bombs before they are loaded onto an FB-111A at Mountain Home AFB, Idaho.

operator beside him in the right-hand seat. Both seats form part of the F-111's emergency escape module, which is pressurized and air-conditioned. This advanced feature is used in place of ejector seats, and allows the crew to escape from the F-111 at any speed and any altitude. The module is separated from the rest of the airframe by an explosive cutting cord activated by either crew member. At this point a rocket motor is fired to carry the module up and away from the crashing airframe before the opening of the parachute that lowers the module, which is stabilized by part of the wing structure that remains attached. Air bags are popped out of the module's bottom to cushion impact with the ground or provide flotation in the water.

The pilot has manual control of the variable-geometry wings that contribute in a major way to the F-111's very impressive combination of short field performance, long range and high dash performance. With the wings in the minimum-sweep position of only 16°, a very heavily laden F-111 can lift off the runway with ease after an impressively short run, aided by the double-slotted flaps on the wing trailing edges and the variable-camber flaps along the full span of the wing leading edges. With the wings in the intermediate-sweep position of 54°, the F-111 achieves high subsonic transit speed combined with considerable fuel economy. With the wings in the maximum sweep position of 72.5°, the F-111 can reach maximum speeds of Mach 2.5 at high altitude or Mach 1.2 at sea level.

Another key to the F-111's performance, this time in the tactical arena, is the terrain-following system that allows it to adopt a high-speed approach to the target at very low altitude. In this system, the small terrain-following radar in the nose under the large search radar is linked to the flight controls through the autopilot. The terrain-following radar emits forward of the F-111 a lobe shaped like a ski-toe. So long as this moves along flat ground, no control commands are made; when rising ground enters the lobe, a pull-up command is given; and when falling ground is encountered, a push-down command is issued. The effect of the system is to make the F-111 parallel the ground in a slightly undulating flight at the altitude selected by the pilot, who can also enter into the

system the degree of ride harshness that is acceptable.

The pilot makes this decision in the knowledge that a harsh ride allows a lower flight profile, but only at the expense of crew concentration and endurance as the greater buffeting affects them; on the other side of the coin, a soft ride dictates a higher flight profile, which reduces buffeting and enhances crew concentration and endurance but only at the expense of greater vulnerability to enemy defence systems.

The F-111F is fitted with a version of the impressive ASQ-133 digital fire-control system also fitted in the A-6 Intruder, and this gives the crew options for manual or automatic weapon delivery with free-fall weapons of various types. This variant also carried the AVQ-26 'Pave Tack' target acquisition and laser designation system. This is carried in the interdictor's small internal bay, which is otherwise used to accommodate an M61A1 Vulcan cannon pack with 2,028 rounds of ammunition, or alternatively two or three 500lb (230kg) bombs.

The 'Pave Tack' package is installed in the internal bay with its power-operated trainable turret head protruding into the airflow beneath the fuselage. This turret accommodates a forward-looking infra-red sensor and a laser designator.

Above: An F-111F interdictor of the 48th TFW, based at RAF Lakenheath, is seen in flight with 'Paveway' bombs.
Below: An F-111F of the 48th TFW releases 500-lb bombs over the Bardenas Reales weapon range in Spain.

Using the FLIR, the weapons system operator can acquire a sharp thermal image of the target under virtually any conditions by day and night, and then magnify the image to allow pinpoint designation with the boresighted laser designator. The turret is then locked onto the target, and a laser-guided bomb is released. The pilot can then depart the scene in the full confidence that the turret is still locked onto the target and illuminating it with the laser radiation needed by the 'Paveway' bomb's guidance system.

The F-111F can carry the impressive maximum of a 31,500lb (14,290kg) weapon load in its internal bay and under the wings, which support six hardpoints each rated at 6,000lb (2,720kg). It is seldom that the F-111F would carry such a load, however, for its most important capability is precision attack of decisive targets (bridges, tunnels, marshalling yards, dumps, command centres etc) deep in the enemy's rear areas, or alternatively chokepoints closer to the battlefront. Attacks

in both these areas would play a significant part in any American interdiction campaign designed to starve front-line forces of reinforcements and supplies.

Further interdiction and operational-level strike capabilities are soon to be added by European deployment of the F-111G. This new variant is being produced as a conversion of the FB-111A, which is now surplus to SAC requirements. The FB-111A was produced as the medium-range strategic counterpart to the F-111A with more powerful engines, role-optimized electronics, beefed-up landing gear, and longer-span wings with eight rather than six hardpoints that permitted the carriage of a maximum 37,500lb (17,010kg) warload including up to six free-fall nuclear weapons, or six examples of the AGM-69A Short-Range Attack Missile (now SRAM-A) or 50×750lb (340kg) conventional bombs.

The F-111G has been made necessary by the 1988 Intermediate Nuclear Forces Treaty, which required the removal from Europe of the BGM-109 Tomahawk ground-launched cruise missile and the MGM-31 Pershing II theatre-level surface-to-surface ballistic missile. This left a considerable operational gap that is to be plugged by the F-111G, which will probably have capability for the AGM-86B air-launched cruise missile, which will almost certainly be replaced in due course by the AGM-129 Advanced Cruise Missile and the AGM-131 SRAM-II successor to the SRAM-A.

The F-111 series is expected to remain in first-line service with the USAF until at least 2010, and the type is still regarded so highly that an extremely costly Avionics Modernization Program is being undertaken to upgrade 120 F-111A/Es, 57 FB-111A/F-111Gs, 166 F-111D/Fs and 38 EF-111As with more capable General Electric attack radar, Texas Instruments terrain-following radar, and a host of improvements to the navigation and control systems. In a parallel programme initiated in 1990 for completion in 1994, all surviving aircraft are being retrofitted with a new and considerably more reliable digital flight-control system.

Above: Bomb-carrying F-15E tactical interdictors cruise over the desert after take-off from Luke AFB, Arizona.
Below: In its several forms, the F-15 Eagle is one of the Tactical Air Command's most valuable operational assets.

Now partnering the F-111 in the attack and interdiction roles, though only over shorter ranges, is the latest version of the McDonnell Douglas F-15 Eagle. This is the F-15E, which is based structurally on the F-15D and marks a radical departure in USAF thinking in being a two-seat tactical interdictor, and therefore far better able to operate effectively in adverse conditions that the single-seat types previously procured.

The origins of the type lie with the manufacturer's own private-venture F-15 Enhanced Eagle, which was produced to persuade the USAF of the advantages possessed by the two-seat formula for the high incidence of poor weather conditions in Europe. In 1984 the USAF selected the McDonnell Douglas type in preference to the General Dynamics F-16XL development of the Fighting Falcon with a cranked-arrow wing for much improved payload/range performance, and the first F-15E flew in December 1986. Originally 396 F-15Es were to have been procured, but this total has been trimmed to 200. The type became operational in 1989 with the 4th Tactical Fighter Wing based at Seymour Johnson Air Force Base in North Carolina.

With its maximum 24,250lb (11,000kg) warload, the F-15E has a shorter radius than the F-111 with the same load, but can carry a considerably wider assortment of weapon types. This gives the F-15E greater versatility than its heavyweight partner, and suits it ideally to the tactical interdiction role. Like the F-15C air superiority fighter, the F-15E carries FAST (Fuel And Sensor Tactical) packs, which are conformal tanks that fit into the angles between the fuselage sides and wing undersides, producing very little drag but providing the ability to carry 9,000lb (4,080kg) of additional fuel and weapons, the latter carried by tangential hardpoints on the lower corners of the FAST packs.

The pilot has a wide-angle head-up display for flight, navigation and tactical data, while the weapons system operator has head-down displays for the radar, forward-

Above, below and bottom: The F-117As flown by the 37th TFW from Tonopah Test Range Airfield, Nevada, offer unique capabilities for successful attack of high-value targets.

looking infra-red, digital map and threat-warning systems. In addition to its APG-70 main radar, used in conjunction with the AWG-27 armament control system, the F-15E's most important nav-attack sensor is the LANTIRN (Low-Altitude Navigation and Targeting Infra-Red for Night) system carried in two external pods. The navigation pod under the port wing accommodates terrain-following radar and a forward-looking infra-red sensor with a wide angle of vision, and the target acquisition and tracking pod under the starboard wing holds a forward-looking infra-red sensor with stabilized narrow and wide angles of vision, together with a laser ranger and designator.

The LANTIRN system gives the F-15E the ability to operate under all day and night weather conditions, and to deliver attacks with dazzling and decisive accuracy.

Another American warplane designed to operate in the deep attack role is one of the least known but most discussed operational assets of the USAF, namely the Lockheed F-117A. This is colloquially known as the 'stealth fighter', but despite its designation in the F (Fighter) category like the F-111, it is solely an attack platform. Developed from 1979 via the Experimental Stealth Technology aeroplane, the F-117A first flew in June 1981 and in October 1983 became the first 'stealth' warplane to enter service.

The 'stealth', or more formally the low-observability, concept encompasses aircraft designed to achieve unimpeded penetration of enemy airspace by avoiding detection. This involves the elimination of active radar as a frequently used system, for radar energy stands out in its part of the electromagnetic spectrum as brightly as the beams of a powerful lighthouse during a dark night. Radar is probably carried, but only for last-minute targeting use, and reliance is therefore placed on passive features such as inertial and/or satellite navigation, and optronic and/or laser target acquisition and designation.

The elimination of such emitters is only half of the low-observability battle, however, for the 'stealth' warplane's airframe and powerplant also have to be designed for minimum detectability. In the case of the F-117A, the concept

adopted for the airframe was that of a V-tailed flying wing of the lifting-body type. This contains a high proportion of radar-absorbent materials to trap rather than reflect much of the energy emitted by the enemy's radars, and a faceted external shape that ensures that any reflected energy is dissipated in all directions but that straight back to the enemy radars. These two factors help to ensure that the F-117A's radar signature is smaller by several orders of magnitude than that of current warplanes of more conventional design, and hence its detectability by radar is very limited and then only at short range. Other features designed to mitigate the F-117A's radar signature are shielded engine compressor faces, and jagged- rather than straight-edged panel junctions in the outer skin.

The F-117A is powered by a pair of General Electric F404 non-afterburing turbofans of low acoustic and thermal signatures. The type's thermal wake is further reduced by shielded slot exhausts which operate, together with heat-shedding tiles, to dissipate heat still further. As a result of its external contours and non-afterburning engines, the F-117A is decidedly subsonic. The design is basically unstable, and control is effected through a 'fly-by-wire' control system. Other electronic elements form the passive nav/attack system, and include a head-up display, at least one head-down display, radar and other warning receivers, and a target-acquisition/marking package that includes two trainable forward-looking infra-red turrets and a laser.

The armament remains classified, but the warload of about 4,000 lb (1,815kg) is carried internally in a pair of lower-fuselage bays. The F-117A's operational rationale indicates that its deep-attack targets would be high-value installations such as command bunkers, communication centres, strategic dumps, and key radar sites. These would be tackled by one or two precision weapons such as the AGM-65 air-to-surface missile, the AGM-88 HARM anti-radar missile, or the

Right: An F-117A in nearly undetectable flight.
Below: An F-117A takes on fuel from a KC-10A
Extender dual-role tanker and transport.

BLU-109 Improved 2,000lb (900kg) Warhead fitted with any of its several laser or optronic guidance packages to become a 'Paveway II' or 'Paveway III' glide bomb with laser guidance, a GBU-15 glide bomb with optronic or imaging infra-red guidance, or an AGM-130 stand-off glide bomb with optronic or imaging infra-red guidance and a rocket motor for extended stand-off range.

It is believed that the F-117A could exercise a decisive part in a future war, for its ability to approach a sensitive target without detection (and therefore without warning the enemy) opens the fascinating possibility of destroying the enemy's command structure. This could be achieved by killing senior military and political leaders at a meeting detected by satellite reconnaissance, or knocking out the cohesion of the

enemy's communication network. This requirement places as much emphasis on effective use of effective weapons as on covert approach to the target, and the F-117A is currently the subject of an important weapons system improvement programme.

Production of the F-117As was completed in July 1990 with the last of just 59 aircraft, and the surviving 56 aircraft are operated by part of the 37th Tactical Fighter wing (until recently the 4450th Tactical Test Group) based at the Tonopah Test Range Airfield on the vast Nellis Air Force Base complex in Nevada. The F-117A is too slow and lacking in range for long-range deployments, and was therefore designed for partial disassembly for transport to its operational area by a Lockheed C-5 Galaxy or Lockheed C-141 StarLifter freighter.

NUCLEAR ATTACK
The Manned Bomber

The United States operates a triad of strategic weapon delivery systems as the cornerstone of its nuclear deterrent policy. These are the submarine-launched ballistic missile, the intercontinental ballistic missile, and the long-range bomber. The last two are the responsibility of the US Air Force, which fields the Minuteman and Peacekeeper unmanned ICBMs from silo complexes in the northern part of the continental United States, and manned bombers from bases in several parts of the country.

Numerically the most important bomber in USAF service is the Boeing B-52 Stratofortress that first flew in prototype form during 1952 and reached operational capability in June 1955. The Stratofortress was designed for the intercontinental strategic role, operating at high altitude with a large number of free-fall nuclear bombs. From 1962 however, the vulnerability of the high-altitude bomber to the increasingly capable surface-to-air missile was recognized and the type was switched to the low-level task. In this role, the free-fall bomb was partially replaced by stand-off missiles such as the AGM-28 Hound Dog. The AGM-69A Short-Range Attack Missile (now SRAM-A) was also adopted as a means of eliminating the defences that might destroy the B-52 before it closed to within Hound Dog range of its primary target.

The older variants are now out of service, and the two current variants are the B-52G and B-52H, which have shorter vertical tail surfaces, a strengthened structure, and considerably greater fuel capacity in a combination of integral tankage and two non-jettisonable external tanks under the wings. These two models equip ten Strategic Air Command bombardment wings, and actual numbers are 165 B-52Gs with 13,750lb (6,240kg) thrust Pratt & Whitney J57-P-43WB turbojet engines and 95 B-52Hs with 17,000lb

Above: The age of the Stratofortress is shown by this shot of a B-52H's cockpit with its mass of dial instruments.

Previous spread: A B-52G Stratofortress of the 43rd Bombardment Wing is serviced on the flight line at Andersen AFB, Guam, before a training sortie over South Korea.
Left: The AGM-86B launch equipment in the OAS station on the lower deck of a B-52G of the 93rd Bombardment Wing

Above: A B-52G of the 60th Bomb Squadron unloads 500-lb bombs at typically low altitude during a bombing exercise.

(7,710kg) Pratt & Whitney TF33-P-3 turbofan engines.

The B-52G is operated in two forms. The more important of these is the stand-off missile role with an armament of 12 AGM-86B air-launched cruise missiles and eight SRAM-As. The AGM-86Bs are carried as two triplets of missiles on each of the underwing pylons originally fitted for the Hound Dog, while the SRAM-As are carried in the internal weapons bay. Some 90 aircraft operate in this configuration, which also permits the AGM-86Bs to be replaced by SRAM-As, while the other 65 aircraft operate in the maritime surveillance and support role with between eight and 12 stand-off anti-ship weapons. These last can be the AGM-84 Harpoon medium-range missile or the GBU-15 guided glide bomb, which is soon to be supplanted by the Israeli-designed AGM-142 'Pop-Eye'.

The B-52H is also flown in the stand-off role, in this instance with 12 AGM-86Bs under the wings, and another eight weapons (AGM-86Bs or SRAM-As) on the Common Strategic Rotary Launcher carried in the weapons bay. Like the B-52G, the B-52H has been considerably upgraded in electronic terms throughout its service life, and is still reckoned to possess the ability to penetrate deep into the enemy's defended airspace. This constant improvement of the Stratofortress's electronic system applies to both the offensive and defensive suites, which are centred respectively on the ALQ-151 Electro-optical Viewing System and the Phase VI Electronic Counter-Measures System. Even so, there can be no avoidance of the fact that with its considerable size, angular design, and eight engines each with an unshielded and therefore highly reflective compressor face, the

Stratofortress possesses a very large radar signature and must therefore be detectable on the enemy's radar screens far too soon for safety.

Even with these system improvements and modern weapons, the Stratofortress has long been recognized as obsolescent in airframe and performance terms in the face of modern air-defence complexes. Thus the Stratofortress has been supplemented in the stand-off role by the Rockwell B-1B, and this has allowed the B-52 to be redeployed in the maritime role, where its considerable range and heavy warload offer unrivalled capability with the weapons already mentioned as well as mines.

Another task that can still be undertaken by the Stratofortress is wholly conventional 'iron' bombing. There is still a demand for this capability, which for some time was considered at best obsolescent and at worst obsolete, in the destruction of fixed defence lines and similar targets. In this role, the Stratofortress can lift a warload of about 50,000lb (22,680kg), which translates into a large number of 1,000lb (455kg) and 750lb (340kg) free-fall bombs for delivery onto tight-packed defensive positions as devastating carpets of high explosive. Such tactics were used in the Vietnam War with the Stratofortress units operating at high altitude, but given the nature of the latest defensive weapons they would now be flown at low altitude with bombs carrying retarder tails and/or delay-action fuses. Like low-altitude tactical warplanes, the bombers need to depart the scene of attack before the bombs' detonation or else face the possibility of destruction by their own attack.

Any B-52 sortie is preceded by standard procedures such as flight planning, briefing, and pre-flight checks of the bomber before the crew board. The men enter by means of a door in the underside of the fuselage in front of the well for the forward unit of the main landing gear, a bicycle arrangement of two four-wheel units. The radar navigator and navigator sit facing forward on side-by-side downward ejecting seats on the lower deck. The other crew men climb the internal ladder to the upper deck, where they are all accommodated on upward ejecting seats: the pilot and co-pilot face forward, while the electronic warfare officer and gunner face aft.

After take-off, the B-52 accelerates to just under 210mph (340km/h) and climbs in the mode that optimizes range, namely a gradual decrease in speed connected to a slow increase in altitude to cruise height. As the bomber approaches enemy territory, the pilot brings his machine down to considerably lower altitude. During peacetime training flights this is generally in the region of 1,000 to 1,500ft (300 to 460m) above the highest obstruction along the planned flightpath for an instrument approach, and between 500 and 800ft (150 to 240m) for a contour-flying approach. In wartime this approach would be flown at somewhat lower but classified altitude, the pilot bearing in mind that even a very modest 20° bank puts the lower wingtip 25ft (7.6m) below the bottom of the fuselage, this figure increasing to 55ft (17m) in a 40° bank.

Contour flying is undertaken with the aid of terrain-avoidance radar or the ASQ-151 EVS, with the pilot keeping both hands on the control column to keep the wings level and course within 2° of planned track, and the co-pilot handling the throttles to regulate airspeed. The size of the B-52, with its wide wings, makes low-level flight most turbulent and uncomfortable, and the two crew members on the lower deck are unhappily aware of their downward-ejecting seats, a legacy of the Stratofortress's high-altitude origins.

The low-level approach flight takes the bomber toward its targets, which can be attacked with a variety of weapons. Air-defence complexes and other secondary targets are engaged at short range by the SRAM-A. This highly supersonic missile has a maximum range of 137.5 miles (221.2km), declining to 35 miles (56km) from a low-altitude launch, and carries a 200-kiloton warhead. The real task of the SRAM-A is clearing a path for the bomber and its major weapons. Until recently these major weapons were free-fall thermonuclear bombs of the B28, B43, B53 and B83 types. The B28 has five yield options between 70 kilotons and 29 megatons, the B43 is a 1-megaton weapon, the B53 produces a 9-megaton blast, and the B83 is believed to have yield in the low-megaton range.

The primary weapon is now the AGM-86B. This is subsonic, but its small size produces only a tiny radar echo and this makes the Air-Launched Cruise Missile a difficult weapon for the enemy to intercept. The weapon flies toward its target in a ground-hugging profile under the control of its inertial navigation system, which is updated by the system's terrain-contour matching unit. This latter compares the radar image of the ground being overflown with data stored in its computer's memory, and thereby assesses deviation from planned course and the correction necessary to bring the missile back on track. The AGM-86B has a range of 1,500 miles (2,400km), and can deliver its 200-kiloton warhead with an accuracy of between 30 and 100ft (9 to 30.5m) after a maximum-range flight. The effect is that a single B-52 can attack between 12 and 20 targets within a radius of 1,500 miles (2,400km).

Right: Ground connections provide air-conditioning, air and power for the crew servicing a B-1B at Dyess AFB, Texas. Far right: A B-1B is marshalled into position at Ellsworth AFB, South Dakota, home of the 28th Bombardment Wing.

The key to successful low-altitude penetration of enemy airspace by the B-52 is the ALQ-151 system. The steerable sensors for the system are accommodated in two bulged fairings under the lower fuselage beneath the flight deck. The port fairing accommodates the low-light-level TV camera and the starboard fairing the forward-looking infra-red sensor. These supply optical or thermal images to the screens in front of the two pilots and the two navigators, though the latters' displays do not incorporate the traces associated with the terrain-avoidance system. The ALQ-151 provides clear imagery for navigation and attack, and in the latter allows external monitoring even when the aluminized window blinds have been lowered against the effects of nuclear flash. ALQ-151 imagery is automatically recorded for post-strike damage assessment.

The emphasis of the B-52G's role is shifting steadily to the maritime role as the B-52H assumes the stand-off role, and this trend away from the high-threat environment is continuing as the B-52H's role of stand-off strike after penetration of enemy airspace is assumed by the B-1B. Just 100 of these capable variable-geometry bombers were procured, and the surviving aircraft are now operated by the 28th Bombardment Wing at Ellsworth Air Force Base in South Dakota, the 96th BW at Dyess AFB in Texas, the 319th BW at Grand Forks AFB in North Dakota, and the 384th BW at McConnell AFB in Kansas.

The B-1 was originally planned as a Mach 2+ supersonic successor to the B-52 in its original high-altitude role, and first flew in this B-1A form during December 1974. The B-1A was of highly curvaceous overall design with General Electric F101 afterburning turbofans aspirated via variable inlets. This powerplant was well matched to the elegant airframe with its variable-geometry wing platform. Thus it was able to lift a sizeable warload from a fairly modest runway with the wings in the minimum-sweep position, to fly over a considerable range with the wings in the medium-sweep position, and to reach a very high speed with the wings in the maximum-sweep position.

As the flight trials continued, the USAF finally admitted the fact that the day of the high-altitude bomber, even in its supersonic form, was not just going but gone. So despite the prototypes' excellent capabilities, the B-1A programme was cancelled by President Carter during 1977.

In 1981 the programme was revived, albeit in considerably altered form, by President Reagan. The new B-1B was a considerably modified type intended for the penetration role at very low level and very high subsonic speed. For this role the airframe was strengthened to withstand the effects of low-altitude buffeting, the landing gear was beefed up to cater for operations at higher weights, and the powerplant installation was modified for a maximum speed of just Mach 1.25. This last involved modification of the nacelles and use of fixed inlets in place of the original variable-geometry inlets.

A great effort was also made to reduce the B-1B's radar signature, which is now thought to be only about one-tenth of that possessed by the B-52. This programme involved the incorporation of radar-absorbent materials in forward-facing areas of the airframe, and the incorporation of S-shaped streamwise baffles in the inlet ducts to shield the compressor faces of the four 30,780lb (13,960kg) afterburning thrust General Electric F101-GE-102 turbofans. The first aerodynamic prototype was a modified B-1A that flew in March 1983, and the first true B-1B flew in September 1984 with the definitive bomber's advanced offensive and defensive electronic suites.

The Offensive Avionics System was developed by Boeing on the basis of its system for the B-52 with APQ-164 multi-mode attack, ground-mapping and terrain-following radar, an inertial navigation system, Doppler navigation and an astro-inertial navigation system integrated via IBM computers and display units. The Defensive Avionics System was a Raytheon responsibility developed as the ALQ-161A with phased-array antennae, reprogrammable digital computers, display units, and jammers for the near-instantaneous detection, analysis, localization and jamming of hostile radars. The OAS has worked with commendable capability and reliability from

early in the programme, but the DAS been plagued with technical problems that still beset the B-1B some time into its service career.

The last B-1B was delivered in 1988, and the type is now operational in the penetration role. In its primary nuclear tasking, the B-1B can operate as a free-fall bomber or as a stand-off missile launcher. The type's typical maximum warload is in the order of 64,000lb (29,030kg), carried in three internal bays rated at a theoretical maximum of 75,000lb (34,020kg) and on six underfuselage stations rated at a combined total of 64,000lb (29,030kg). Internal weapon stowage clearly keeps the B-1B's radar signature as small as possible, and use of the internal bays allows the B-1B to operate as a bomber with 12 of the USAF's older thermonuclear bombs (B28 and B43) or 24 of the service's newer bombs (B61 and B83), or as a missile carrier with eight AGM-86Bs, or 24 AGM-69As or, most likely, a mix of these two missile types.

The underfuselage stations can carry eight B28 bombs, or 14 B43, B62 and B83 bombs, or 14 AGM-86B and AGM-69A missiles.

The B-1B can also be flown in the conventional bombing role, and here the weapons bays can carry 24×2,000lb (910kg) or 128×500lb (225kg) bombs while the underfuselage hardpoints can lift 14×2,000lb (910kg) or 44×500lb (225kg) bombs.

Thus the B-1B carries basically the same weapon types as the B-52, but with the AGM-129A Advanced Cruise Missile and the AGM-131A SRAM-II in prospect as replacements for the AGM-86B and AGM-69A. When not used as a penetration free-fall bomber with thermonuclear bombs carried internally, the B-1B is generally flown as a missile carrier with a typical load of eight AGM-86Bs in the weapons bays (together with SRAM-As and additional fuel tankage) and another 14 AGM-86Bs on the underfuselage hardpoints. The B-1B flies much same type of flight profile as the B-52, but at lower altitude and higher speed. In themselves, these factors make the B-1B a better penetration bomber and missile-

launching platform than the B-52. The ALQ-161A DAS also offers the possibility of improved penetration capability, but only if and when the technical problems with this advanced system have been cured.

It was planned that the B-1B should be supplanted in the penetration role by the Northrop B-2A 'stealth bomber' from the mid-1990s, and then move into the stand-off and conventional bombing roles that are now the preserve of the B-52. However, the extent of the B-2A's operational service is at present undecided, and it could well be that the B-1B will have to soldier on in its penetration role for considerably longer than first envisaged, though this will have the advantage of allowing the ALQ-161A system to be made fully effective!

The B-2A was designed at enormous cost in a highly secret 'black programme' during the late 1970s and 1980s, and was first revealed in November 1988 for an initial flight in July 1989. This fascinating bomber is being developed as the successor to the B-1B in the penetration bomber role. Unlike the low-altitude B-1B, however, the B-2A is designed for penetration of enemy airspace at medium and high altitudes, relying on its 'stealth' design and composite structure to

Above: The B-2A is a new and exciting shape in the sky, but while it offers superb offensive capabilities the type may still prove too expensive and politically 'hot' for more than a small number to be built and placed in service.

evade detection by enemy air defence systems (including optronic and infra-red sensors as well as radars) until it has closed to within a few miles of its target.

Like the F-117A attack warplane, the type was planned round the concept of a non-emitting approach to the target with navigation entrusted to inertial and satellite navigation systems. It was clear that the B-2A is unlikely to remain undetected over the target, however, and so radar can be used in the terminal phase of the attack for extreme accuracy of navigation and targeting. The main APQ-181 radar has features in common with the APG-70 system used in the F-15C, D and E versions of the McDonnell Douglas F-15 Eagle, and is an advanced equipment of the synthetic-

Below: A left-side view of the first B-2A as it prepares for its maiden flight at the Air Force Flight Test Center, Edward AFB in California, during July 1989

aperture type with 21 operational modes including coherent mapping.

The B-2A is a design of the relaxed-stability type, and is a flying wing with 40° swept but straight leading edges and W-shaped trailing edges featuring simple flight-control surfaces (elevons for pitch and roll control, and 'differential drag' surfaces for yaw control) operated by a fly-by-wire control system. The B-2A is unlike the F-117A in overall design concept, for whereas the F-117A was based on 'stealth' by faceted external contours, the B-2A is conceived round completely smooth surfaces with blended bulges for the two-man flightdeck and engine nacelles. Radar reflectivity is very low because of the use of radiation-absorbent materials and a carefully optimized shape (including jagged-edge panel joins and shielded upper-surface inlets), and a head-on radar cross section in the order of only 10.76 sq ft (1.00m²) has been quoted for the B-2A in comparison with about 107.64 sq ft (10.00m²) for the B-1B and some 1,076.37 sq ft (100.00m²) for the B-52. In addition, the careful mixing of hot exhaust gases with cold freestream air before release through the type's two-dimensional nozzles reduces thermal and acoustic signatures to a very significant degree in this firmly subsonic design.

In common with its F-117A partner in the American 'stealth' family, the B-2A is designed to carry its warload internally, for only thus can a smooth external shape be maintained. The B-2A has two side-by-side weapons bays for the carriage of an 80,500lb (36,515kg) maximum payload. It is believed that each weapons bay can accommodate an eight-round Strategic Common Rotary Launcher for a maximum of 16 AGM-131A SRAM-II missiles or B83 free-fall thermonuclear bombs, the most advanced American weapons of their types. Other loads are thought to include up to 20 examples of the B61 thermonuclear bomb, with conventional 'iron' bombs as another possibility.

Production of 132 B-2As was planned to create an operational force that would carry some 2,000 of the 4,845 strategic nuclear weapons in the USAF's inventory. The US Department of Defense's 1989 review of the services' financial

Above: As part of its development, the B-2A proved its air refuelling capability, in this instance from a KC-10A.

commitments in the face of the enormous American budget deficit includes amongst its provisions the proposal that the service debut of the B-2A be postponed for at least one year to save on financial outlay and also allow additional time for development of this extremely ambitious and complex warplane. In 1991 it became increasingly likely that political opposition, rising production costs and further financial constraints would probably limit procurement of the B-2A to a mere 75 machines.

In mid-1990 it was revealed that the USAF is to task its B-2As with a secondary maritime surveillance and attack role with weapons such as the AGM-84 Harpoon anti-ship missile, though this task may be eliminated if the total B-2A procurement is limited to just 75 aircraft. The advantage of the B-2A over the B-52 in this maritime role is the ability of the 'stealth' bomber to fly higher while remaining undetected, thereby improving fuel economy (and thus range) and enlarging the 'sensor grazing area' that allows the long-range detection and engagement of ship targets.

It is also worth noting that American strategic operations rely heavily on air-to-air refuelling to provide the bombers with adequate range. For this reason, all the USAF's inflight-refuelling tankers are organizationally a part of Strategic Air Command. Current tanker strength is some 635 or more old but updated and still very capable Boeing KC-125A/E/R Stratotankers and 59 McDonnell Douglas KC-10A Extenders. The latter is a larger type that also possesses an important secondary transport tasking. Each bombardment wing has its own tanker force drawn from the 39 regular Air Force, Air Force Reserve and Air National Guard squadrons that operate such aircraft. Inflight-refuelling is also very much a part of the Tactical Air Command's operational requirements, and the USAF has a flexible system that allows the diversion of a considerable part of SAC's tanking capability to TAC.

UNARMED IN BATTLE
Electronic Warfare

American warplanes almost bristle with the antennae of offensive and defensive electronic systems, and on the whole are well able to operate over the modern battlefield with its host of surface-based and air-carried electronic systems. Even so, it is clear that protection of warplanes against ground-based electronic systems often demands that the warplane sacrifices much of its payload to secure electronic protection that is at best only just adequate. This means that many tactical aircraft have to use one or more hardpoints for electronic pods, which results in the carriage of a smaller warload, or alternatively reduced performance (in terms of speed and range) because of the drag generated by the electronic pod or pods. American tactical planners also have to bear in mind that while the large number and assortment of podded systems available to their tactical aircraft can and do provide a high measure of electronic protection, such podded systems can never match the quality and versatility of dedicated electronic warfare platforms.

For this reason the US Air Force and US Naval Aviation each operate a small number of dedicated electronic warfare platforms. These aircraft are complex and extremely expensive, but offer tactical capabilities of unparalleled sophistication and operational effect. As such, therefore, these electronic warfare aircraft fulfil a number of roles in support of packages of tactical attack and strike aircraft.

The EA-6A is now used only in small numbers by US Naval Aviation and the air arm of the US Marine Corps, which have respectively just 15 and six examples of the type in service. The naval aircraft are used mainly for electronic intelligence-gathering and training, and while the marine corps aircraft have a theoretical operational tasking, they are in practice used only for training.

It became clear soon after the EA-6A's debut that while the type was very useful, it lacked the overall capabilities needed in a stand-off electronic warfare platform, and as a result the manufacturer developed a truly optimized version of the Intruder as the Grumman EA-6B Prowler, the different name emphasizing the newer type's very considerable alteration from the Intruder.

The EA-6B first flew in May 1968 as the prototype of a powerful stand-off electronic warfare platform for the US Navy. The airframe was still based on that of the A-6A, but was increased in length by some 4ft 6in (1.37m) and strengthened for operations at higher weights as a result of extra fuel capacity and the addition of the complex but extremely versatile and capable ALQ-99 Tactical Jamming System for the detection, location, classification and jamming of hostile radars. The additional fuselage length was required for a longer four- rather than two-seat cockpit, which is now occupied by the pilot and navigator/systems operator (side-

The first of the modern electronic warfare aircraft to enter service was the EA-6A variant of the Grumman A-6 carrierborne medium strike/attack warplane. Like its offensive half-brother, the EA-6A is still called Intruder. The type was developed as a strike/attack support platform able to operate alongside the Intruder warplane. The type is powered by two 9,300lb (4,220kg) thrust Pratt & Whitney J52-P-8A/B turbojets. This variant retains a partial attack capability, but is used solely for the support role as a tactical jamming aircraft. As such the EA-6A carries the 30 antennae of the ALH-6 and ALQ-86 receiver/surveillance systems to detect, locate and classify enemy radars which can then be jammed by the onboard ALQ-31 noise, ALQ-53 track-breaking and ALQ-76 noise jammers; the EA-6A also carries the ALE-32 internal chaff dispenser to swamp enemy radar screens with echoes. The EA-6A also carries the Intruder family's full complement of five external hardpoints, and these can be fitted with electronic countermeasures pods if required.

Previous spread: Two EF-111A Ravens of the 366th TFW taxi to the flight line at Sachon AB in South Korea.

by-side in the two front seats) and the two dedicated systems operators (side-by-side in the two rear seats).

Production aircraft were delivered from January 1971 with the first model of the TJS. In this system, receiver antennae in the fintop fairing pick up electromagnetic emissions from a hostile radar or radars, and pass the data to the central digital computer. Here the signals are displayed on the system operators' screens and recorded. The system's computer then identifies the type of radar, and fixes its bearing (and its position by means of triangulation). The nature of the radar's emissions is analyzed automatically (with the manual mode available as a back-up should the operators so decide) to determine the required jamming set-on frequency. Finally, any one of the five external jamming pods is activated. Each pod is powered by a windmill generator on its nose, covers one of seven frequency bands, and contains two powerful jammers.

Electronic developments since the time of the Prowler's advent have been rapid and very far-reaching, yet the EA-6B remains a key component of the US Navy's strike/attack capability as a result of the succession of improvement programmes which have enhanced the capability of the initial

Above: This shot of an EA-6B Prowler landing on the Kitty Hawk *reveals the type's externally-carried jammer pods.*
Left: An air-to-air shot of an EA-6B Prowler of VAQ-130 'Lancers' in flight over the Pacific Ocean

variant. This was based on the ALQ-99A system with an AYA-6 computer, and was capable of dealing only with single radars in four frequency bands. Evolution of the TJS then produced a series of improved standards. The EXCAP (Expanded Capability) standard of January 1973 has the ALQ-99B system for the jamming of radars in eight frequency bands and a capability for automatic coverage of multiple threats. The ICAP-1 (Improved CAPability-1) standard of March 1976 has the ALQ-99C(V) system using digitally tuned receivers and computer-controlled subsystems for the jamming of several emitters forming a complete weapon system. The ICAP-2 (Improved CAPability-2) standard of January 1984 has the ALQ-99D(V) system using the AYA-14 computer (offering four times the memory and three times the speed of the AYA-6) for the jamming in nine frequency bands of several weapon systems forming a defence complex, and fitted with the DECM (Defensive Electronic Counter-Measures) suite plus provision for four missiles on four underwing hardpoints. Finally, the ADVCAP (ADVanced CAPability) standard for service from 1992 has the Litton ALQ-99F(V) system using a more capable signal processor, the AYK-14 computer and an Amecom (Litton) receiver and processor group operating in 10 frequency bands for improved jamming of communications, three ALE-47 chaff/flare/decoy dispensers in place of the baseline model's single ALE-39

Below: EA-6B Prowlers of Carrier Air Wing 14 undergo shore-based servicing during Exercise 'Gallant Eagle '88'.

dispenser, and the ALQ-149 voice and data communications jammer, plus provision for six missiles on six underwing hardpoints.

Current Prowlers have been retrofitted with the capability to carry two AGM-88A HARM anti-radiation missiles under the wings. This gives the type the ability to kill rather than just direct enemy radars.

The EA-6B is still under steady improvement, and other features to be added include a receiver suite for the Global Positioning System and the Joint Tactical Information Distribution System. The GPS is an automatic system using a network of satellites to broadcast the signals interpreted by the receiver to provide position data accurate to just a few yards. The JTIDS is a completely secure voice and digital data communications system that is highly resistant to enemy jamming, and able to 'talk' with compatible systems operated by all the American forces and by some of the United States' allies.

Other items slated for incorporation on the Prowler, but which may now not be fitted, at least in the near future, included the ALQ-165 Airborne Self-Protection Jammer that was cancelled in 1990 because of technical problems. The US Navy is also planning to fit the 12,000lb (5,445kg) thrust J52-P-409 turbojet into the Prowler. This engine, known to its manufacturer as the PW1212, is an improved version of the basic J52 with features of the civil JT8D engine offering faster response to throttle movements, greater fuel economy and stall-free operation. The additional power of this improved engine is needed to offset the greater drag of the EA-6B Prowler ADVCAP's larger fintop and new underfuselage antennae groups, and therefore maintain the performance of the EA-6B at about the same level as that of the A-6E/TRAM Intruder. Other modifications in this 65,000lb (29,585kg) aircraft will be centred on aerodynamic enhancement such as drooped leading-edge slats, wing root leading-edge strakes, a taller vertical fin and modified wingtip speed brakes/ailerons.

In the 1990s the aircraft are to be retrofitted with the ALQ-149 TCCS (Tactical Communications Countermeasures System), an automatic system carried internally for

Below: An EF-111A Raven, or 'Electric Fox', of the 42nd Electronic Combat Squadron is seen in flight over England.

the detection, identification, evaluation, localization and jamming of hostile communications and long-range early warning radars.

US Naval Aviation and the air arm of the US Marine Corps have respectively 150 and 12 examples of the Prowler in service or on order for 14 and one operational squadrons. The carrier air group of each US Navy aircraft-carrier operates five Prowlers, a number sufficient to provide stand-off support to any strike/attack package launched by the parent ship against a land or sea target.

The US Air Force's equivalent of the Prowler uses a repackaged version of the ALQ-99 TCS. Though colloquially known as the 'Spark Vark' or 'Electric Fox', this air force model is more properly known as the Grumman/General Dynamics EF-111A Raven. This is a conversion by Grumman of the obsolescent F-111A initial production of the 'Aardvark' variable-geometry interdictor, and is similar in overall concept to the Prowler in being a derivation of the strike/attack type most likely to need and receive the support of the conversion.

The EF-111A's raison d'etre is basically identical with that of the EA-6B, namely electronic warfare support for American packages of strike/attack warplanes, and in particular the F-111 long-range interdictor. The need for such a type was appreciated in the early 1970s, and it was only logical to award the development contract to Grumman with Raytheon as main subcontractor responsible for the electronic aspect of the programme. It was clear from the beginning that the F-111A could not be subjected to the same type of fuselage lengthening as the A-6A, so the ALQ-99 TJS was revised as a fully automated system. At the same time it was appreciated that the Prowler's assembly of up to five self-powered jammer pods would degrade the Raven's performance to the level that it might not be able to support supersonic F-111s, so a semi-conformal jammer package was developed.

The aerodynamic features of the Raven were evaluated in a flight test programme that began in December 1975, but it was March 1977 before the first EF-111A flew. Even this was only an aerodynamic prototype used to prove the combination of the large fintop fairing for the receiver antennae and the ventral 'canoe' fairing for the jammer antennae. Thus the first true prototype was the second EF-111A that flew in May 1977.

Above: Distinguishable by its fintop antenna fairing, an EF-111A takes on fuel from a KC-135's 'flying boom'.

Finally the first of 42 'production' conversions flew in June 1981, just before the activation of the first Raven squadron.

The heart of the EF-111A's operational capabilities is the Tactical Jamming System which, as noted above, is the Prowler's three-man system repackaged in ALQ-99E(V) computer-assisted form for one-man operation, and developing sufficient power to overwhelm the world's most intense radar defences. The fairing at the top of the vertical tail surfaces houses the forward-, side- and aft-facing receiver antennae of the TJS, while the ventral 'canoe' fairing, projecting below the volume that was the internal weapons bay of the F-111A, accommodates the main body of the TJS together with its six digitally tuned receivers, five exciters and 10 jamming transmitters. Other systems are the ALQ-137(V)4 deception jammer, the ALR-62(V)4 terminal threat-warning receiver, the ALE-40 chaff/flare dispenser, the ALR-23 countermeasures receiver system, and (for possible retrofit) the ALQ-131 jammer system in pods under the wings.

The Raven can thus support tactical aircraft as an escort, in the penetration role or as a stand-off jammer. The type may be retrofitted to carry the AGM-88 HARM radiation-homing missile on its four underwing hardpoints, and the ALQ-99E electronic system is being upgraded in concert with the ALQ-99 system of the Prowler.

The Raven is allocated to Tactical Air Command, and the type's operator units are the 390th Electronic Combat Squadron of the 346th Tactical Fighter Wing, based at Mountain Home Air Force Base in Idaho, and the 42nd Electronic Combat Squadron based at RAF Upper Heyford in the United Kingdom. The 390th ECS is responsible for crew training, though its aircraft and crews have a high-priority operational tasking in time of war, while 42nd ECS provides British-based F-111 interdictors with operational support. This last was proved with a high degree of success in April 1986, when Ravens of the 42nd ECS paved the electronic path for the F-111s launched from British bases to attack targets in northern Libya and so deter Colonel Ghaddafi from support of further terrorist activities against American interests in Europe.

The Raven has three main operational tasks. In the stand-off task, the Ravens move into an orbital flightpath in friendly air space, well to the rear of the forward edge of the battle area and thus safe from the attentions of enemy surface-to-air missiles. With their orbit established, the Ravens start to broadcast jamming signals designed to swamp the enemy's radars and so mask the arrival of the supported strike/attack package and its subsequent penetration of enemy airspace.

In the penetration task, the Ravens escort the aircraft of the strike/attack package when the target to be attacked lies deep in the enemy's rear areas. In this task, the Ravens remain with the F-111s or other attackers throughout the mission, broadcasting continuously to 'knock out' the enemy's electronic defence systems. In this task, the compatibility of the Raven's performance with that of other supersonic strike/attack aircraft is very important.

In the close air support role, the Ravens also escort their charges. Here speed and range are not important, for the Ravens are operating over or close to the battlefield, using their electronic system to aid subsonic tactical warplanes such as the Fairchild Republic A-10A Thunderbolt II.

THE LOOKOUTS
Airborne Early Warning

The cutting edge of American strategic and tactical air power rests with large numbers of powerful and constantly updated warplanes delivering advanced weapons with the aid of thoroughly up-to-date optronic and/or electronic nav/attack systems. In itself this vast military strength could be decisive, yet its capabilities are greatly enhanced in defensive as well as offensive missions by the availability of airborne early warning aircraft. These are often called 'force multipliers', for their presence so boosts the effective use of warplanes in their area that it is almost as though there were many more warplanes available.

These airborne early warning aircraft patrol the skies, using their long-range active and passive electronic systems to build up a complete picture of the air situation. The size and completeness of this picture allow tactical crews on board the airborne early warning platforms to control the overall nature of the American air activity in any given situation. Here the tactical crews use secure voice and/or data-link communications with ground stations and airborne warplanes to direct the overall pattern of the evolving air battle, and this allows air assets to be used most economically without the need for obsolescent tasks such as wide-ranging fighter patrols that consume fuel, use up airframe and maintenance time, and tire crews without any advantage being gained.

The two airborne early warning platforms currently in service with the American forces are the Boeing E-3 Sentry and Grumman E-2 Hawkeye. The Sentry is used by the US Air Force, which procured a total of 34 such aircraft, while the Hawkeye is a carrierborne type operated by the US Navy, which has 110 or more of the type in service. The two types are radically different in size and powerplant, but offer not dissimilar operational capabilities.

One of the most expensive but important aircraft in the current military inventory, the Sentry is a highly capable AWACS (Airborne Warning And Control System) plane designed for three-dimensional surveillance of a massive volume of air and the direction of all American and some allied operations within that volume. The original E-3A is based on the airframe of the Model 707-300B airliner, and two EC-137D prototypes were delivered for operational evaluation of the Westinghouse APY-1 and Hughes APY-2 radars in competition as the Sentry's primary sensor. The Westinghouse radar was judged superior, and this type was selected for installation in the overfuselage radome of the E-3A production aircraft which began to enter service in March 1977. The last of the 34 aircraft was delivered in 1984.

The first 24 aircraft possess the capability to operate only over land, and this type is designated Core E-3A. The model has pulse-Doppler radar, a CC-1 computer, nine situation display consoles, two auxiliary display units and 13 communication links. The last 10 aircraft are designated Standard E-3A and possess additional sensor capability that provides the ability to operate over water, a faster-working CC-2 computer with a 665,360-word memory, secure voice communications capability, and the Joint Tactical Information Distribution System.

The E-3A has proved remarkably successful in operational service, but the pace of electronic development since the advent of the Core and Standard models has now made these types not so much obsolescent as approaching the edge of this state. The USAF sees the technical and tactical importance of keeping its important 'force multipliers' as close to the technological leading edge as possible, and the E-3A has been steadily updated. The Core E-3As and the two EC-137Ds have been improved to E-3B standard with the CC-2 computer, the situation display consoles increased in number from nine to 14, the JTIDS voice and data communication system, the

Previous spread: An E-2C Hawkeye is silhouetted against the sun as it lifts off from the Nimitz *for its long patrol.*
Below: The US Air Force's equivalent of the US Navy's Hawkeye is the E-3A Sentry, and such a force multiplier is seen here as it takes off from Kadena AB in Japan.

'Have Quick' secure communications system, improved electronic counter-measures capability, and limited overwater sensor capability.

The standard to which the Standard E-3As are being raised is the E-3C. This has five extra situation display consoles (as in the E-3B), additional UHF radio gear and the 'Have Quick-A' communications system. This model also has the capability to carry small underwing pylons, which could carry AIM-9 Sidewinder air-to-air missiles for a modest self-defence capability.

This last signals the USAF's tardy recognition that though the Sentry is designed to stand back from the scene of main air activity and use its long-range surveillance radar to watch the situation, the enemy will inevitably make the most strenuous efforts to knock out the all-important 'force multipliers'. This means that fighters must be kept within rapid diversion range of any AWACS platform so that it can be protected against any enemy fighters that break through toward it, while a last-ditch self-defence capability is provided by the Sidewinders and the infra-red jammer of the Sentry's Improved Self-Defense System.

The heart of the Sentry's operational capabilities lies in its primary sensor, the APY-1 surveillance radar. The antenna for this system is 24ft (7.3m) wide and 5ft (1.5m) high, and this provides the Sentry with its most distinctive feature, the large black and white rotodome carried over the rear fuselage. This rotodome is 30ft (9.1m) in diameter and 6ft (1.8m) in height, and turns at 0.25 revolutions per minute when the radar is not in use but at 25 revolutions per minute when the radar is in use. Within the rotodome, the radar antenna is backed by the antenna for the APX-103 system, which combines Identification Friend or Foe and Tactical Digital Intelligence Link – Command functions. The complete system provides for the location and identification of all aircraft within a large radius of the Sentry. The radar and IFF/TADIL-C data are fed

Above: Maintenance personnel service an E-3 of the 552nd Airborne Warning & Control Wing at Tinker AFB, Oklahoma. Below: Royal Australian Air Force personnel watch operations in a 961st Airborne Warning & Control Support Squadron E-3.

to an IBM 4 Pi high-speed computer (CC-1 or faster-operating CC-2 versions depending on the specific Sentry variant). The CC-1 model is capable of 740,000 operations per second, and has main and mass memories of 114,688 and 802,816 words respectively.

In the E-3A, the results are fed to nine multi-purpose and two auxiliary display consoles. The Sentry cruises at an altitude of between 28,000 and 30,000ft (8,500 and 9,100m), and at this height the radar can detect targets such as a ground-hugging fighter or cruise missile out to a range of 265 miles (426km). The range of the Sentry's radar allows the type to orbit beyond the range of enemy surface-to-air missile

Above: E-3s of the 552nd AW & CW at Tinker AFB.
Below: An E-2C of VAW-121 'Bluetails' is seen on a patrol protecting the carrier Dwight D. Eisenhower.

systems but yet see comparatively deep into enemy territory and thereby gather comprehensive radar data. This allows the tactical crew to build up a complete picture of air activity and control friendly aircraft in the most effective manner.

The Sentry is generally flown by a three-man crew (pilot, co-pilot and navigator) with the tactical compartment in its fuselage occupied by a 12-man mission crew (communications operator, computer operator, nine radar operators in three transverse rows, and a radar maintenance engineer). A mission crew of 16 is possible, and the additional men are highly appreciated on longer-endurance sorties. The standard mission duration is about 10 hours (translating into a six-hour patrol at a radius of 1,000 miles (1,600km) from base), but the Sentry has inflight-refuelling capability and can thus remain airborne for very much longer periods in which the main limitation is crew fatigue. This is a particularly important factor with aircraft such as the Sentry, which is fitted with a crew rest station fitted with aft-facing seats, bunks, a galley and a lavatory.

The USAF's Sentry force is operated by Tactical Air Command. The parent organization for the force is the 552nd Airborne Warning & Control Wing, which is based at Tinker Air Force Base in Oklahoma. At this base the wing has one training and three operational squadrons. The operational squadrons are the 963rd, 964th and 965th Airborne Warning & Control Squadrons, while the training squadron is the 966th AW & CS. The wing also controls squadrons that are

permanently based at Elmendorf AFB in Alaska (the 562nd AW & CS), at Kadena Air Base in Okinawa (the 961st AW & CS) and at Keflavik AB in Iceland (the 960th AW & CS). For operational purposes, TAC's Sentries come under the control of major commands such as Alaskan Air Command, the Pacific Air Forces, and the US Air Forces in Europe.

The USAF's Sentry is a substantial machine based on a swept-wing airliner and powered by four 21,000lb (9,525kg) thrust Pratt & Whitney TF33-P-100/100A turbofans for a maximum speed of about 580mph (935km/h). The US Navy's Hawkeye is an altogether different machine designed specifically for its exacting role and yet offering no problems to carrierborne operations and accommodation. The type is straight-winged and powered by a pair of 4,910 or 5,250shp Allison T56-A-425 or -427 turboprops for a maximum speed of 374mph (600km/h). The Hawkeye can be refuelled in flight, and its operational capabilities include a four-hour patrol at a radius of 200 miles (320km) from its parent carrier. Given its smaller size and endurance, the Hawkeye carries a smaller crew than the Sentry, in the form of a flight crew of two in the cockpit and a mission crew of three in the cabin. The type is operated by 17 squadrons.

The Hawkeye predates the Sentry in original concept, and was designed in the late 1950s as an advanced replacement for the interim airborne early warning platform then operated by the US Navy. The fact that the Hawkeye replaced a

Below: An E-2C of VAW-115 'Sentinels' and an F/A-18A of VFA-192 'Golden Dragons' from the elderly carrier Midway.

comparatively simple airborne early warning platform should not be taken, however, as any indication that the Hawkeye is just an improved airborne early warning type. The Hawkeye certainly does fulfil this task, but also possesses the sophistication to operate as a flying control post, and this makes the Hawkeye a force-multiplying airborne warning and control system platform.

The type first flew as the W2F-1 prototype form during October 1960 and entered service in January 1964 as the E-2A Hawkeye to provide the US Navy with exceptional multi-role capability through the use of the APS-96 radar with its antenna in a revolving rotodome above the fuselage. The improved E-2B was introduced in 1969 by converting E-2As first with a superior digital computer and then with the more capable APS-120 radar, which added an overland capacity to the APS-96's basic overwater capability. The variant also added provision for inflight-refuelling, and introduced enlarged vertical tail surfaces.

The definitive version of the Hawkeye is the E-2C, which began to enter service in November 1973 after the first flight of a prototype in January 1970. This variant introduced the APS-125 radar able to detect aircraft at ranges of 230 miles (370km) even in ground clutter, and able to perform the simultaneous detection and tracking of more than 250 ship and aircraft targets while controlling 30 or more interceptions at the same time. The radar incorporates an advanced electronic counter-counter-measures capability to defeat the effect of the tactical jamming systems carried by enemy tactical aircraft.

It should be noted, however, that later E-2Cs have the still

more advanced APS-138 radar with low sidelobes and active-element arrays to permit automatic and simultaneous tracking of up to 600 targets out to a range of 300 miles (480km). These aircraft also feature a passive detection system (initially the ALR-59 electronic support measures system and from 1980 the improved ALR-73 ESM system) for the automatic detection, plotting and identification of electronic emitters in a high-density environment at ranges up to 500 miles (800km).

The provision of data-link equipment allows the secure transmission and receipt of information between E-2Cs and other aircraft or surface vessels.

From 1988 the standard radar has been an improved version of the APS-138, namely the APS-139 with enhanced capability to detect slow-moving and indeed stationary targets such as warships. From the early 1990s production aircraft will be delivered with the new APS-145 radar, while older aircraft are to be retrofitted with this system. The APS-145 is under final development as a radar system able to operate effectively over normal rather than comparatively featureless terrain.

The importance of the Hawkeye to US Naval Aviation is attested by the composition of the typical 86-aircraft carrier air group. Such a group contains 34 attack aircraft (two squadrons with 24 Vought A-7 Corsair IIs or McDonnell Douglas F/A-18 Hornets, and one squadron with 10 Grumman A-6 Intruders), 16 anti-submarine aircraft (one squadron of Lockheed S-3 Viking fixed-wing aircraft and one squadron of Sikorsky SH-3 Sea King or SH-60 Seahawk helicopters), 24 fighters (two squadrons of Grumman F-14 Tomcats or F/A-18 Hornets), and 12 force-multiplying aircraft (four examples each of the Grumman KA-6D Intruder inflight-refuelling tanker, Grumman EA-6B Prowler electronic warfare platform, and Hawkeye warning and control platform). Some aircraft-carriers carry five examples each of the Prowler and Hawkeye.

The task facing this small complement of fighters is enormous, for it must not only provide escort for outgoing and incoming strike/attack packages, but also protect the financial and operational investment represented by the parent carrier against attack by aircraft and missiles. This is ensured only by the availability of the Hawkeye, whose force multiplication capabilities make it possible to use the fighters most effectively.

After briefing, aircraft checks and catapult launch, the

Below: A member of an E-2C Hawkeye's tactical crew tracks the movements of surface vessels on his radar screen during drug surveillance operations.

Above: An E-2C touches down on the Independence *during carrier qualifications by Reserve Carrier Air Wing 30.*

Hawkeye climbs steadily at just over 200mph (320km/h) to its cruise altitude. As fuel is burnt off in this 30-minute ascent to 27,100ft (8,260m), the rate of climb increases from 2,515 to 3,290ft per minute (12.78 to 16.71m/s). The patrol position is centred on a point about 230 miles (370km) from the parent carrier toward the most likely threat, and at a height of about 27,600ft (8,410m) at a speed of slightly more than 300mph (480km/h). Once the Hawkeye is in position, the pilot switches to the automatic flight control system, and this allows the Hawkeye to orbit along an oval track 58 miles (93km) long and

11.5 miles (18.5km) wide. The Hawkeye generally operates in pairs, the two aircraft flying orbits that generate overlapping search areas to reduce the task of enemy attackers 'leaking' through the radar surveillance.

The three mission crew men have already unlocked their seats and swivelled them from the forward-facing position mandatory for take-off. Now the seats face toward the port side of the fuselage, the location for the instrument and display consoles operated by the combat information centre officer, the air control officer, and the flight technician.

If an incoming track is seen, the possible threat is interrogated by the Identification Friend or Foe system. This can confirm if the incomer is hostile, and the same conclusion

can be reached if the incomer activates its electronic counter-measures system in an effort to blind the Hawkeye's radar. The Hawkeye is now in communication via data-link to its parent carrier, the fighter on combat air patrol in this sector, and a lurking EA-6B Prowler. By triangulation the Hawkeye and Prowler confirm the attacker's exact position, and this can be data-linked to the nearby F-14 Tomcats, one of which can destroy the target with a long-range AIM-54 Phoenix air-to-air missile.

This is only the simplest of possible scenarios, but such is the overall capability of the Hawkeye that it can monitor and control the whole extent of the offensive and defensive air and sea battle that might develop around a carrier battle group.

EYES IN THE SKY
Tactical Reconnaissance

Reconnaissance is an absolute necessity for all aspects of military activity, and this is particularly important at the operational and strategic levels. Only on knowledge of the enemy's strengths and dispositions is it possible to make any realistic assessment of his intentions. For many years both the US Navy and USAF were also able to undertake strategic reconnaissance, but with the retirement of the former's Rockwell (North American) RA-5C Vigilante and the latter's Lockheed SR-71A 'Blackbird' this capability disappeared. The services now rely on satellite and other information to complete their strategic assessments, and so far as aircraft are concerned they are therefore left with tactical reconnaissance types that can to a certain extent also undertake the operational reconnaissance role.

It is worth noting, however, that the American forces operate a large number of specialist reconnaissance platforms quite distinct in type and basic capability from the aircraft discussed below. Such aircraft range in size from the substantial Boeing RC-135 with four jet engines to the comparatively small Beech RC-Huron with two turboprops. These aircraft are operated in modest numbers along the coasts and frontiers of potential enemies, using their state-of-the-art, vastly expensive, highly classified and frequently updated electronic systems to listen to the enemy's communications, electronics, signals and telemetry.

At the tactical level, the most important reconnaissance type in American service is the McDonnell Douglas F-4 Phantom II. This is flown by the air arm of the US Marine Corps which has 25 or more examples of the RF-4B in service

Below: Operators monitor the radar consoles of an NKC-135. Previous spread: An RF-4C Phantom II of the 18th Tactical Reconnaissance Wing is connected to its starter unit in preparation for a nocturnal mission.

with VMFP-3, a squadron based at Marine Corps Air Station El Toro in California, and by the USAF which has 325 or more examples of the RF-4C in service with 15 squadrons allocated to Tactical Air Command (five squadrons in the continental United States), the United States Air Forces in Europe (two squadrons based in Germany and the United Kingdom), the Pacific Air Forces (one squadron based in Okinawa), and the Air National Guard (seven squadrons based in the continental United States).

The RF-4B and RF-4C are both fully role-optimized versions of the Phantom II, and carry their primary specialized equipment internally rather than in the external pods that give other tactical aircraft a reconnaissance capability. Podded systems can be switched from warplane to warplane as required, and therefore offer considerable operational flexibility, but the quality of the reconnaissance data secured by such podded systems is often inferior to that of fully optimized internal systems.

The RF-4B is the second oldest surviving operational variant of the legendary Phantom II series, and first flew in March 1965 as a tactical day/night photo-reconnaissance platform derived from the F-4B fighter. The type is unarmed and has a lengthened nose which accommodates radar as well as providing additional volume for forward and oblique cameras; infra-red reconnaissance equipment is also carried. In the second half of the 1970s the SURE programme updated surviving RF-4Bs with the ASN-92 inertial navigation system for improved navigational accuracy, together with the APD-10 side-looking airborne radar and the AAD-5 infra-red reconnaissance system; at the same time the ALQ-26 electronic counter-measures system was installed.

Above: Ground crew secure the camera installation of an RF-4C at Bergstrom AFB, Texas.
Right: The TR-1A reconnaissance platform in flight.

The RF-4C is the USAF's precursor to and counterpart of the RF-4B, and as such is the oldest Phantom II variant in service. The type is a tactical reconnaissance version of the F-4C with the missile and bomb delivery systems removed, and the nose modified to produce an overall length of 62ft 11in (19.18m) with the additional volume required for reconnaissance equipment. The demonstrator for this variant first flew in August 1963, and the type was first flown in production form during May 1964. The RF-4C is generally equivalent to the RF-4B with forward-looking radar, the APQ-102 side-looking airborne radar, the AAS-18A infra-red linescanner, and a combination of high- and low-altitude panoramic, forward and oblique cameras.

Some aircraft have been updated with the ALQ-125 Tactical Electronic Reconnaissance package for the detection, identification and localization of the enemy's air-defence radars in a manner analogous to the APR-38 system of the F-4G 'Wild Weasel' version of the Phantom II. This type has the ALR-17 electronic counter-measures receiver, the APR-25 homing and warning system, the AAQ-4(V) infra-red jammer, the ALQ-162 radar jammer, and provision for podded items such as the ALQ-71, -72 and -87 jammers now replaced by the ALQ-101 as well as later electronic counter-measures systems.

It has been recognized for some time that the RF-4 is obsolescent, and as the type is disappearing from more warlike service its maintenance will become increasingly difficult. Yet the concept of developing a reconnaissance variant of the service's most important tactical warplane remains valid, and the USAF is to replace its RF-4C with the RF-16C version of the General Dynamics F-16 Fighting Falcon.

Recent developments in reconnaissance technologies have made it feasible for modern tactical reconnaissance platforms to use podded systems rather than inbuilt equipment. In the RF-16C, therefore, development emphasis is being placed on such podded systems so that airframe changes can be minimized. The primary reconnaissance sensor is the Advanced Tactical Air Reconnaissance System, whose pod combines an optronic sensor and an infra-red linescanner with a secure digital data-link so that the system can download its findings to a ground station on a real-time basis. The real-time receipt of reconnaissance information by its users is immensely important at the tactical level. Subsequent analysis of the information can correct initial misinterpretations and add more information, so the ATARS pod also contains a digital recorder.

The US Navy's tactical reconnaissance capability is currently restricted to an interim type, the Grumman F-14A/ TARPS Tomcat. This simple adaptation of the basic F-14A fleet defence fighter was necessitated by the retirement of the RA-5C Vigilante. In this version, a few Tomcats of each carrier air group are fitted under the fuselage with the LA-160 Tactical Air Reconnaissance Pod System. This contains an AAD-5 infra-red linescanner, a KS-87B frame camera and a Fairchild KA-99 low-altitude panoramic camera.

The F-14A/TARPS is to be upgraded with the ATARS pod as noted above, and this will give carrier battle groups adequate tactical reconnaissance. Superior capability will be offered by a definitive tactical reconnaissance platform, however, for the RF-4B is to be replaced by a variant of the F/A-18D two-seat night attack derivative of the F/A-18C single-seat fighter

Below: The Rockwell OV-10A Bronco is a simple yet effective type used as a forward air control platform, spotting and marking targets and then radioing the co-ordinates and other tactical information to the aircraft tasked with undertaking the attack. Here the crew of an OV-10A from the 25th Tactical Air Support Squadron at Eielson AFB, Alaska, directs the efforts of two A-10A Thunderbolt IIs during the 'Calfex IV' combined Army and Air Force exercise at the Yukon Command Training Site in Alaska.

and attack platform.

This RF-18D is to be the US Marine Corps' carrierborne and land-based reconnaissance type. Production of 83 such aircraft is planned, each carrying a version of the Advanced Tactical Airborne Reconnaissance System pod on its centreline hardpoint under the fuselage. This version of the ATARS pod will contain the UPD-4 side-looking airborne radar, an advanced synthetic-aperture type. Data from this pod, as well as from the carrying aeroplane's standard optical and infra-red sensors, will be transmitted to a ground station via a real-time data-link.

The US Army has only a few fixed-wing aircraft designed for operation over the battlefield. The most important of these is the service's main tactical reconnaissance type, the

Below: The latest forward air control type in US Air Force service is the OA-10A version of the Thunderbolt II, which is replacing the OA-37 version of the Cessna A-37 Dragonfly, itself a derivative of the T-37 'Tweet' side-by-side trainer. Seen over the desert of the south-west United States, this is an OA-10 of the first unit to convert to the newer type, the 23rd Tactical Air Support Squadron that is the main component of the 602nd Tactical Air Control Wing based at Davis-Monthan AFB in Arizona.

Grumman OV-1 Mohawk, of which about 140 or more are in service. This is an easily identified type with triple vertical tail surfaces, two turboprops, and bulged cockpit sides so that the pilot and systems operator have good fields of vision obliquely downward to each side of their aeroplane.

All earlier variants of the Mohawk in service with the US Army for battlefield reconnaissance have now been upgraded to the OV-1D standard with strengthened structure and more powerful engines, and offering the reconnaissance capabilities of the original OV-1B with the APS-94 side-looking airborne radar and the OV-1C with the AAS-4 infra-red surveillance system in a single airframe. The original OV-1A had a span of 42ft (12.8m) and first flew in April 1959, but the current type with a span of 48ft (14.6m) offers considerably improved flight as well as reconnaissance capabilities. The choice between side-looking airborne radar and infra-red primary sensors is complemented by an updated vertical panoramic camera for photographic reconnaissance.

A variant of the OV-12D for the tactical reconnaissance and electronic intelligence roles is the RV-1D. Twelve such aircraft have been produced by converting OV-1Bs with the ALQ-133 'Quick Look II' target locator radar system and the Northrop ALQ-162 radar jammer.

INDEX